INVESTIGATIONS INTO GENERATION
1651–1828

INVESTIGATIONS INTO GENERATION 1651–1828

*

ELIZABETH B. GASKING

THE JOHNS HOPKINS PRESS
BALTIMORE

Published in Great Britain by
Hutchinson Publishing Group Ltd.
178–202 Great Portland Street
London W1

Library of Congress Catalog Card Number 66–16041

Contents

I

Introduction

'Observation and experience can and must drastically restrict the range of admissible scientific belief, else there would be no science. But they cannot alone determine a particular body of such belief. An apparently arbitrary element, compounded of personal and historical accident, is always a formative ingredient of the belief espoused by a given scientific community at a given time.'

Kuhn, THE STRUCTURE OF SCIENTIFIC REVOLUTIONS

A MODERN biology textbook will contain no reference to a special subject called generation. Yet the term (or its Latin equivalent) was used in connection with certain biological studies from antiquity until the beginning of the nineteenth century. It is purely an historical accident that the word itself has disappeared, for today there is no lack of interest in the topics which were once considered under this heading. Indeed, they are achieving a new unity as the science of genetics gradually expands to include all the different enquiries which were touched on by the earlier investigations into generation.

In its most restricted sense the term 'generation' was used to indicate the coming into existence of new individual organisms, both animal and plant, irrespective of the method which might be involved. When the matter was first considered it was known that all the animals we now call mammals reproduce sexually, but some at least of the lower animals were supposed to develop spontaneously from mud or warm water. It was recognised that plants can grow from seed and from a variety of vegetative parts, but, since plant sexuality was not understood, no clear distinctions could be drawn between these different types of reproduction. Immediately generation in this primary sense became a subject for study a host of new questions came to be asked, which caused the investigations to spread out in all directions.

In the case of animals which reproduce sexually, the initial problems concerned the contributions made by the different sexes: does the new individual grow out of a material entity contributed by the male and merely nurtured by the female? Or does the female provide the entity, and if so, what role does the male play? If both contribute, what is the nature of these contributions? The embryo develops gradually, but what does it look like at the different stages and in what order do the parts appear? All organisms seem to grow from structureless primordia into complex organic structures, each one being of a very definite kind. How is it that the structureless primordium of a deer grows into a deer, while that of a dog develops into a dog? How do the appropriate parts develop in the proper relative positions? The offspring are of the same kind as the parents, but are not, in general, exact replicas. In respect of certain characteristics an offspring may take after one parent or the other, in certain minor ways it will differ from both. What are the laws which govern the appearance of these individual characteristics? Occasionally a widely deviant 'monster' is produced: What can be the cause of such an abnormality? During the eighteenth century the phenomenon of animal regeneration was considered for the first time, and it was noticed that many animals can regenerate lost parts and that some of the simpler types can actually produce new individuals from subdivided fragments. Between the re-growth of a claw or a tail and the formation of a new individual there was no clear distinction; hence the phenomenon of regeneration was included within the study of generation.

These are only a sample of the many diverse problems which were raised once generation was studied in detail. Clearly, they touch on many different topics. Equally clearly, they have an essential unity—for they are all concerned with the very general and very central problem of organic growth and differentiation.

Not all these problems were raised at once, but, because the power to reproduce is such an obvious and remarkable characteristic of living things, a surprisingly large number of them did appear very early in the history of biology. Aristotle, the greatest Greek biologist, was intensely interested in generation and a large proportion of his extant biological works are concerned with the subject. However, it is quite clear from the copious references which he made to the views of his predecessors that even in his time the subject already had a long history. On the other hand, one has only to reflect upon the nature of the research which is being carried out today to see that it is still concerned with topics which might be classified as aspects of generation.

This book deals with the history of the investigations into generation between 1651, when Harvey published his work on the topic, and 1828, when von Baer announced his discovery of the mammalian egg. In view of the fact that the subject has such a long history, what justification can there be for isolating a relatively short period and concentrating attention upon it? The answer lies in part in some fairly recent changes in the historiography of science. Today most historians of science would agree that while some subjects may have a long and even a continuous history, in the sense that there has always been an interest in this particular aspect of nature, it does not follow that they show a continuous logical development from the past to the present. Nor does it follow that each phase of their history can or should be viewed as a direct contribution to our modern approach. From the earliest times some men have been interested in the nature of the heavenly bodies just as others have been interested in the reproduction of living things, and in both cases there has been a gradual accumulation of factual knowledge. But the sort of questions asked at the different periods and the kinds of explanations required have been too variable for it to be possible to see either the astronomy or the biology of the past as an immature version of the modern science. Once this idea is accepted there is no need to deal with all stages of the development of a science as a single unit.

The historian is free to deal more fully and in a slightly different way with more specific topics and with particular and shorter periods. Professor Kuhn has summed up this change in the following way:

> Gradually, and often without entirely realising that they are doing so, historians of science have begun to ask new sorts of questions and to trace different, and often less than cumulative, developmental lines for the sciences. Rather than seeking the permanent contributions of an older science to our present vantage, they attempt to display the historical integrity of that science in its own time. They ask, for example, not about the relation of Galileo's views to those of modern science, but rather about the relationship between his views and those of his group, i.e. his teachers, contemporaries and immediate successors in the sciences. Furthermore they insist upon studying the opinions of that group and other similar ones from the viewpoint—usually very different from that of modern science—that gives these

opinions the maximum internal coherence and the closest possible fit to nature.

(44)

The history of science, and particularly the history of biology, is a relatively new discipline which has undergone many changes of method within a short time. When people first turned their attention to it, it probably seemed a fairly straightforward matter which raised no methodological problems. Most of the early writers aimed at giving a complete history of all aspects of their subject. They described each eminent scientist in chronological order, dealing in turn with what they regarded as his most important discoveries and then appending a short summary of his theoretical views. As pioneers their works have often been very valuable, but the overall impression created by such histories can be extremely misleading, for even this type of history involves both selection and evaluation. What in fact tended to happen was that in the selection of the discoveries made by the historical figures great weight was attached to those which the author, with his present-day attitude to the subject, regarded as important. These were not always those which had the most significance at the time, nor were they necessarily understood by their makers in the way we should understand them today. The theoretical views were described without any attempt to link them with the facts or with the more general outlook of the period. As a result of this treatment, scientists of the past often appeared to be inconsistent and unreasonable. If the background conditions were very unlike our own, the reader tended to feel that these scientists were holding absurd theories which were not supported by the known facts, and it was easy to conclude that many of them must have been moved entirely by some extra-scientific considerations or beliefs.

A second and more sophisticated type of history of science avoided the mistake of treating a man's theories and his discoveries as if they were unconnected. It concentrated on showing the clash between two theories at certain strategic turning points in the history of science. Such histories can be very illuminating, and they can give new insights into the conditions that are necessary to bring about a change in the scientific outlook. But if too much attention is given to these turning points these histories too can be misleading. This is especially true as the turning points selected almost always culminate in the acceptance of the modern view. If all historians concentrate on the Copernican revolution in astronomy, on the development of classical dynamics in physics and on the acceptance of the idea of evolution in biology, they will mislead their readers in at least two ways. The reader of such histories, predisposed to the views which were eventually accepted, is always ready to write off all the opposition as due to mental inertia. He is too seldom able to see that, within the context of their times, the partisans of the older views might have had good scientific grounds for their opposition. In addition, such histories make the progress of science look too easy. Science does not advance at the speed that these histories suggest, nor is it a continuous series of battles in which the 'correct' theory always triumphs over the 'wrong'.

Most modern historians of science would, I think, agree with these criticisms and try to avoid such obvious errors. But, because there are some misleading ways of writing about the history of science, it does not follow that there is any one right method. As more attention has been paid to this aspect of history, the problems raised have become more complicated and the range of interests has become more diverse. Some historians have traced the interconnections between the scientific outlook at certain times and other facets of man's thought. Others have concentrated on the effects of certain scientific discoveries on technological and economic development. The more specialised historians of science tend to concentrate on problems which arise from within the sciences. Some study the development of particular concepts, while others analyse the work of individual scientists. This book belongs to the last category, for in it I am chiefly concerned with the interconnections between the factual information and the theoretical opinions advanced by the different biologists. I hope the book will not merely tell of an interesting set of investigations, but will also throw some light upon the different factors which influenced these scientists and determined their beliefs.

If a study is to be considered scientific, it must give considerable weight to the established or accepted facts. Views on the relative importance of the factual elements in science have differed at different stages and there are always minor differences between individual scientists working at the same time. To take the extreme cases, if a man were to show a complete disregard for all fact we would not describe his work as scientific. Nor on the other hand should we regard a mere catalogue of facts as scientific. Yet even the distinction between the predominantly factual elements—the observations, the empirical data or the phenomena—and the theoretical part of a science, is open to objections. Most scientists and philosophers do make use of some distinction of this kind when they discuss science, but in practice the elements interlock in a very complicated way. In fact, very few statements made in science can be checked by direct observation alone, nor are they usually expressed in everyday language. In the highly developed branches of modern science, where the whole experimental procedure is the direct results of the theory, the dichotomy becomes very blurred. But, in spite of the objections which can be levelled against the distinctions, it has its uses, provided that these qualifications are kept in mind.

In the cases that I shall consider, most of the observations are recorded in a technical language, since ordinary language does not extend to the anatomical details of animals and plants. But this technical language involves very little theory. Moreover, in this relatively simple science, the distinction between fact and theory can be drawn with more ease than it could be if the science under discussion were modern genetics or advanced physics.

No scientist working in any branch of science can ignore the facts; it is the facts which he must collate and explain. But the selection of the facts themselves and the type of explanation which he supplies will be influenced by a very wide and diverse set of factors. This is especially true of this work on generation for, as we have seen, the questions which can be raised by this study are very varied and many are central to biology. Such a scientist is likely to be influenced, for instance, by the prevailing views on the nature of a species. If his contemporaries all assume that species, once created, are thereafter quite unchanging, his interest in generation will be in explaining how like comes to reproduce like, and he will regard deviations from the specific type as 'monsters'—abnormalities to be explained away. If, on the other hand, the men of his time assume that species change, and are interested in how one kind can turn into another, then the specialist in generation is likely to be primarily interested in the ways in which offspring can differ from their parents—so much so indeed, that he may seem almost to overlook the obvious fact that dogs beget only dogs.

Work on generation is also likely to be affected by the general opinion of the time on the nature of the basic structural elements of which all living things are composed. At certain periods, for instance, biologists in general thought of bodily organs as the basic elements, at other times they took tissues to be the biological building stones, and in recent times cells. For any student of generation prior to the cell theory the following problem arose: all living matter is a structure composed of organs (tissues), but the first beginning of a new individual, the primordium, seems to have no structure at all—how then can it be a living thing, if it has no organs (tissues)? When the cell theory is accepted this problem vanishes, for the primordium is then itself supposed to be one of the ultimate units—the cells.

A person's theories on generation and his ways of interpreting the observed facts are liable to be influenced by considerations yet more general. He might hold, for instance, that all parts of all living things are under the direction of a vital spirit or entelechy, or he might, on the other hand, hold that in all nature there is ultimately nothing but inanimate matter and motion. How he explained the phenomena of generation would obviously differ in these two cases. If, like Buffon, he held that there are ultimately two distinct kinds of matter, and also believed in explaining the behaviour of wholes in terms of their constituent parts, he would obviously try to explain generation in terms of the basic animate particles.

People and periods differ in the *style* of explanation they find satisfactory. Aristotle recognised four 'causes'—four different types of explanation. At times 'formal causes' have been much in vogue—a given state of a certain thing was regarded as satisfactorily explained only if it was shown how that state had grown out of an earlier state of the same thing, according to certain very general laws of development. At other times an explanation, to be satisfactory, had to reduce the behaviour of a whole into that of its ultimate parts, and had to give the 'efficient cause' of any change. Some people have insisted on the explanation being in terms of simple forces, attractions and repulsions, and have demanded that everything be explained in terms of the working of such a machine as a clock. Views of such very wide generality, affecting theories in every branch of science, are not inaptly called 'metaphysical'. Those who hold them, however, often simply tacitly take them for granted, without ever stating them explicitly, much less offering arguments in their defence.

In any particular field of biological enquiry, such as the nature of generation, a number of factors combine to determine which theories a man will regard as worthy of credence, and which lines of investigation he thinks promising and important. The first is the experimental facts that are available to him; the second is the general biological outlook and interests of his time, in so far as he shares them; and thirdly he will certainly be influenced by the general views he has of science as such, and of the style of explanation which is proper to it. One cannot properly understand a man's acceptance of one theory and rejection of another, nor is one in a position to assess the reasonableness of his opinions, unless one takes at least these factors into account.

In this book I shall take another look, in light of this kind of analysis, at the ideas about generation which were current in the seventeenth and eighteenth century. I say 'another look' because this part of the history of biology has already attracted considerable attention and has always been mentioned in the general histories. Some aspects of it have been discussed by nineteenth century biologists such as Huxley, Whitman and Wheeler and by modern writers such as Bentley Glass, Joseph Needham and Jean Rostand. The main work on the subject is Professor Cole's *Early Theories of Sexual Generation*. No-one who follows in Professor Cole's footsteps can ever sufficiently acknowledge their debt to him. His care and accuracy has made his work an enduring classic. But Professor Cole's book was published in 1930 and meanwhile, due to the work of many scholars, our knowledge of the general intellectual background of this period has greatly increased and, as we have seen, the historiography of science has undergone many changes. Perhaps, therefore, it is not too presumptuous to feel that another book on the subject is not completely redundant.

My interest in the seventeenth and eighteenth centuries' views on generation was aroused some time ago because I was puzzled and could find no adequate answer to my puzzle in the available texts. On the one hand I had read short accounts of the different theories of generation which were current at this time. All these seemed extraordinarily crude and, at first sight, atypical of the period. On the other hand, the scientists who accepted these views were, in many cases, men of considerable stature, whose experimental work and methodological approach seemed to be of a high standard and completely in accord with the best traditions of Newton and Harvey. How could these two apparent inconsistencies be resolved? Was there some extra scientific reason for their beliefs? Were there some scientific factors which I had overlooked? Or was it perhaps the case that little attention was really given to this aspect of biology during the seventeenth and eighteenth centuries? I already knew that generation had attracted the attention of scientists since the earliest times and a glance at the contents of the learned journals of this period showed that, far from being a casual interest, it was in fact a central issue.

The following chapters give the results of my researches into this problem. I think this research has at least helped me to clarify my original perplexity and has also taught me more about what happens when scientists become interested in aspects of a problem which they lack the means to solve.

2

Harvey and the Breakaway from the Theories of the Ancients

of Harvey Himself

Live Modern Wonder and be read alone
Thye Brain hath Issue, though thy Loins have none
Let fraile Succession be the Vulgar Care
Great Generation's Selfe is now thy Heire.

of Harvey's Ideas on Generation

And for Belief, bids it no longer begg
That Castor once and Pollux were an Egge;
That both the Hen and Housewife are so matcht,
That her Son born, is only her Son hatcht,
That when her Teeming hopes have prosp'rous bin
Yet to conceive is but to lay, within.

Llewellyn, DEDICATION TO HARVEY, 1651

WHEN Harvey (1578–1657) published his work on generation in 1651 he was over seventy years old, but it is clear from internal evidence as well as from reference made to the foetus in *De Motu Cordis* that he had been interested in the subject for a long time, perhaps even from his student days in Padua. Thus the work, when it appeared, was no product of Harvey's old age, but the result of many years' hard work.

During Harvey's lifetime the scientific revolution had been successfully launched and Harvey was an ardent disciple of the 'new' method of studying nature by direct observation and experiment. He realised more clearly than most of his contemporaries that the ancients themselves had used direct observation when forming their theories; perhaps this was because he was a biologist and it is in this field that Aristotle showed himself to be an especially good observer. Harvey was always at pains to point out that he was reviving rather than inventing the so-called 'new' method of observation. All his other works are evidence of this and no-one reading Harvey can doubt that he was fully aware of all that the method implied and of the contrast it provided to the methods of his immediate predecessors. But it is also clear from the introduction to *De Generatione* that he regarded this last work as equally exemplifying the new method and as being a worthy example of it, for he says:

> What shall I deliver in these, my exercises on animal generation, I am anxious to make publicly known, not merely that posterity may there perceive the sure and obvious truth, but further, and especially, that by exhibiting the method of investigation which I have followed, I may propose to the studious a new and unless I am mistaken a safer way to the attainment of knowledge.
>
> For although it is a new and difficult road in studying nature, rather to question things themselves than, by turning over books, to discover the opinion of the philosophers regarding them, still it must be acknowledged that it is a more open path to the secrets of natural philosophy, and that which is less likely to lead into error.
> (*38*, Introduction, p. 152)

Harvey's contemporaries and immediate successors agreed with him about this book: but strangely enough most historians of science have, during the last seventy years, dismissed *De Generatione* rather contemptuously. Thus, Nordenskiold remarks:

> This conservatism of Harvey's displays itself conspicuously in a work which he published in his old age: *Exercitationes de Generatione Animalium* (1651). . . . But above all he proves himself to be a follower of Aristotle whose conceptions of the true essence of life he has made entirely his own.
> (*58*, p. 117)

Even specialists in this aspect of biology like Needham and Cole do not seem to appreciate the enormous importance of this book. Needham, after giving a summary of it, nevertheless emphasises:

> He did not break with Aristoteleanism, as a few of his predecessors had already done, but on the contrary, lent his authority to a moribund outlook which involved the laborious treatment of unprofitable questions.
> (*54*, p. 149)

Cole is, however, much fairer when he says:

> It is a difficult and almost invidious task to review Harvey's work on generation. His demonstration of the circulation of the blood gives him such an exalted position in British science that we are almost tempted to forget his work on generation—in which a great man was making an heroic, and almost pioneer, attempt to solve a problem which was insoluble by his generation, or for that matter by ours. Hence it is inevitably a record of failure.
> (*11*, p. 134)

It is the last sentence which contains one reason for the lack of appreciation of this work. Harvey's observations showed that all previous views on generation were without foundation and his suggestions influenced all subsequent investigations. In spite of this his positive achievements were less impressive. From the vantage point of three hundred years much that Harvey discovered has not, for various reasons, stood without need of qualification.

Harvey's reputation has not suffered for this reason alone. Much of his work has been completely misunderstood and in some cases an almost traditional misinterpretation of his aims has been accepted. Some of these misunderstandings will be dealt with later, but there is one which, since it has little to do with Harvey's main thesis, should be removed at once. His dictum 'Ex Ovo Omnia' has been continuously quoted and mis-quoted (for details of misquotations see *11*, p. 137) and with the passing of time it has gradually become associated with the dispute about the possibility of spontaneous generation. In this case, Harvey has been wrongly credited with being the first to deny spontaneous generation, but he has also been blamed for his lack of clarity on the subject. Yet neither Harvey's work, nor this dictum, are in any way directly concerned with the question of spontaneous generation. The ancients had all accepted the idea that some plants and animals could arise without any previous parents from the mud, and many had also believed that when the higher animals died their bodies automatically decomposed into simpler living things. These ideas had not been questioned at the time Harvey wrote, nor did Harvey really question them. Nowhere in *De Generatione* does Harvey recount any empirical enquiry he has undertaken which would bear on this question. Spontaneous generation is only mentioned in passing, since Harvey's investigations were entirely on organisms known to be sexually reproduced. Once, quite casually, he mentions the possibility that some plants and animals, believed to be produced spontaneously, may well have arisen from seeds or eggs so small that they can be carried unnoticed in the air:

> But on these points we shall say more when we show that many animals, especially insects, arise and are propagated from elements and seeds so small as to be invisible (like atoms flying in the air), scattered and dispersed here and there by the winds; yet these animals are supposed to have arisen spontaneously, or from decomposition because their ova are nowhere to be found.
> (*38*, b, Ex. 41, p. 321)

Harvey does not return to the subject, nor at any stage furnish the promised demonstration. However, he complained that his work on insects was lost when his London house was searched during 'the troubles'. Elsewhere, he usually includes spontaneously generated animals as a possible group. Sentences starting with remarks like 'now the whole of these, whether they arise spontaneously or from others . . .' and 'whence some animals are spoken of as spontaneously reproduced, others are engendered by parents' (*38*, b, Ex. 62, p. 451) are common throughout the book. These suggest an implicit acceptance of this mode of production, but apart from a few casual passages such as those quoted, the matter is not further discussed. Harvey does, however, insist, as we shall see later, that even if animals are spontaneously reproduced without parents each one must nevertheless start life as a simple, undifferentiated primordium and gradually develop and differentiate out.

Before considering the true aim of Harvey's book we must say something about the views of his predecessors. In the introduction to *De Generatione* Harvey himself gives an excellent summary of their views. This is what he says:

> Physicians following Galen, teach that from the semen of the male and female mingled in coition the offspring is produced, and it resembles one or the other, according to the predominance of this one or that; and further that in virtue of the same predominance it is either male or female. Sometimes they declare the semen masculinum as the efficient cause, and the semen feminum as supplying the matter, and sometimes they advocate precisely the opposite doctrine. Aristotle, one of nature's most diligent enquirers, however affirms the principles of generation to be the male and

female, she contributing the matter, he the form; and that immediately after the sexual act the vital principle and the first particle of the future foetus, viz. the heart in animals that have red blood, are formed from the menstrual blood in the uterus.
(*38*, b, Introduction, p. 151)

Now, at the time Harvey was writing, and at all times prior to this, these theories were held in a completely straightforward way. In all cases it was assumed that there must be a mass of material present in the uterus immediately after copulation and that it was from this mass that the new organism was produced. Indeed there seemed to be ample evidence for this: ancient scientists were all acquainted with the quantity of semen ejaculated by male mammals and with the periodical discharge of menstrual blood by the human female. They knew, moreover, that the menstrual flow ceased in pregnancy. These simple facts seemed proof enough that there must be a mass of material present in the uterus from which the offspring was formed.

This was no isolated assumption. It was the basis of all their theories, which all agreed in taking viviparous generation as typical, and interpreting all other kinds of reproduction using this as a model. All equally affirmed that sexual generation was to be understood on the analogy of their assumption about man. The theories differed with respect to the fate of this initial mass within the uterus. Did it all form the embryo? Galen and the Atomists answered Yes. For them the joint product of the two semina coagulated about various points, and gave rise to the most important organs—the heart, the liver and the brain. For Aristotle only the menstrual clot provided the actual matter; the semen in the uterus acted on this and produced from it the first living parts. Once the embryo was formed it grew, nourished by the additional blood provided by the mother. This, incidentally, explained why the menstrual flow in women ceased during the whole pregnancy.

When the development of the chick was being considered, the same model was applied. Here the theories again diverged, and indeed there were many different interpretations. Galen assumed that the yolk represented the joint male and female secretions and gave rise to the chick, while the white provided the additional nourishment. Aristotle suggested that the white was the essential female contribution and the origin of the chick itself, while the yolk supplied the food to be used later. Many suggested that the chalazae were the male semen.

Fabricius insisted that they were in fact the matter from which the chick was formed, and therefore, the true female secretion, the later nourishment being, in his view, provided by both the yolk and the white.

The main thesis of Harvey's work on generation was that the central fact on which all previous theories depended was not true. There was no mass of semina to be found on dissection in any animal, and hence all the previous theories were untenable. Thus the first words of the introduction to *De Generatione* were:

> It will not, I trust, be unwelcome to you, candid reader, if I yield to the wishes, I may even say entreaties of many, and in these exercises on animal generation, lay before the student and lover of truth what I have observed on this subject from anatomical dissections, *which turns out to be very different from anything that is delivered by the authors, whether philosophers or physicians.* (*38*, b, Introduction, p. 151).

There follows an account of the previous theories, quoted above, and immediately following this account Harvey concludes:

> But that these are erroneous and hasty conclusions is easily made to appear; like phantoms of darkness they suddenly vanish before the light of anatomical enquiry. Nor is any long refutation necessary where the truth can be seen with one's proper eyes.
> (*38*, b, Introduction, p. 151)

Within the text is an account of the work done by Harvey which led him to these conclusions. The first part of the book describes the production and incubation of the hen's egg. Harvey gave an account of a hen's ovaries and noted the 'yolks' in various stages of ripeness. He described how the ripe yolks broke away from the ovaries and passed one after another down the distended infundibula to the uterus, gradually increasing in size and acquiring the coverings of albumin, of membranes and of shell until they were extruded. Like Fabricius, he noticed that this increase came about without the egg adhering to the uterus (as Aristotle had assumed), or growing by means of any system of umbilical vessels. He also noted that the entrance to the uterus could not be distended easily from below and that after copulation there was no mass of semen in the uterus. He pointed out that had the semen penetrated to the uterus as was generally believed, it could not there effect any contact with the eggs which were already encased within their shells. He examined fertile eggs and 'wind' eggs (i.e. those produced by the hen which has had no contact with the cock) and could see no visible difference between them when they were first laid. In the newly laid eggs he noted a small white circle on the yolk which Fabricius had called the cicatricula. Fabricius had supposed this to be a scar left when the yolk broke away from the ovary, but Harvey identified it correctly as the point of origin of the chick. He summed up these investigations in relation to the previous theories as follows:

> Yet to him who dispassionately views the question it is quite certain that there is no prepared matter present in the uterus, nor any menstrual blood to be coagulated at the time of intercourse by the semen masculinum as Aristotle will have it, neither does the chicken originate in the egg from the seed of the male nor from that of the female, nor from the two commingled.
> (*38*, b, Ex. 15, p. 228)

If the investigations into the hen's egg suggested that the previous theories were incorrect, Harvey's enquiries into fertilisation in mammals were even more conclusive. He did in fact dissect many different mammals, but the bulk of his work was done on the deer which he was able to obtain from the Royal Parks. He examined both the male and female genital systems in detail, often comparing them with the corresponding human parts. He was unable to observe any changes in the ovaries (which he referred to as the female testicles or glands) when the does were on heat nor could he see anything equivalent to the 'yolks' produced by the hen. He therefore concluded, of course wrongly, that these mammalian organs produced nothing of importance for generation. However, he paid particular attention to the does during and just after the rutting season and after many dissections convinced himself that there was nothing in the uterus immediately after copulation. There was no mass of semen, and no visible material which could be identified as the female contribution to the embryo, nor anything resembling a menstrual clot. Summing up he says:

> Nothing, however, can be discovered there [i.e. in the uterus]—neither the semen of the male, nor aught else having reference to the conception . . . the males have been doing their duty all the while; nevertheless reiterated

> dissection shows nothing. This is the conclusion to which I have come after many years of observation.
> (*38*, b, Ex. 67, p. 477)

And again:

> Repeated dissections performed in the course of the month of October both before the rutting season was over and after it had passed, never enabled me to discover any blood or semen or trace of anything either in the body of the uterus or in its cornua.
> (*38*, b, Ex. 68, p. 478)

Harvey then described the changes which ensued in the uterus wall, and how, about six or seven weeks after the end of the rutting season, he was eventually able to identify, in one or both cornua, the beginnings of the embryo in the form of a 'long-shaped pudding full of fluid stuck by glutinous matter to the wall'. Again he emphasised that at no time prior to this could he find the expected mass of material within the body of the uterus. This, of course, surprised him, and all to whom he mentioned it, including King Charles I.

> Having frequently shown this alteration in the uterus to his majesty the king, as the first indication of pregnancy, and satisfied him at the same time that there was nothing in the shape of semen or conception to be found in the cavity of the organ, and he had spoken of this as an extraordinary fact to several about him, a discussion at length arose; the keepers and huntsmen asserted at first that it was but an argument of a tardy conception occasioned by the want of rain. But by and by when they saw the rutting season pass away, I still continuing to maintain that things were in the same state, they began to say that I was both deceived myself and had misled the king and that there must of necessity be something of the conception to be found in the uterus. These men, however, when I got them to bring their own eyes to the enquiry, soon gave up the point. The physicians, nevertheless, held it among their impossibilities that any conception should ever be found without the presence of the semen masculinum or some trace remaining of a fertile intercourse within the cavity of the womb.
> (*38*, b, Ex. 68, p. 480)

Harvey then conducted, with the king's permission, an experiment to confirm his observations. Towards the end of the rutting season, he segregated more than a dozen does which could reasonably be expected to have been served by the bucks. He killed a few at random and opened up the uteri to show that these were in the state he had described. He then enclosed the rest in a place where no bucks could reach them. Eventually they all fawned, showing that, when enclosed, they were already pregnant in spite of the fact that none of the sample inspected showed the expected evidence in their wombs.

This confirmed Harvey's observations and he now felt justified in concluding:

> In the dog, rabbit and several other animals, I have found nothing in the uterus after intercourse. I, therefore, regard it as demonstrated that after fertile intercourse among viviparous as well as oviparous animals, there are no remains in the uterus either of the semen of the male or female emitted in the act, nothing produced by any mixture of these two fluids, as the medical writers maintain, nothing of the menstrual blood present as 'matter' in the way Aristotle will have it; in a word, that there is not necessarily even a trace of the conception to be seen immediately after a fruitful union of the sexes. It is not true, consequently, that in a prolific connexion there must be any prepared 'matter' in the uterus which the semen masculinum, acting as a coagulating agent, should congeal, concoct and fashion or bring into a positive generative act, or by drying its outer surface include in membranes. (*38*, b, Ex. 68, p. 481)

There is no doubt that Harvey regarded these researches into the early stages of the embryos of birds and mammals as his most important contributions to the study of generation. It is to these, and to these only, which he refers in his introduction to the work. He was, of course, completely wrong in believing that, because there was no identifiable mass of semen in the uterus, no part of it penetrated into this organ or beyond. And he was equally in error when he argued that, since he could see no visible body given off by the mammalian ovaries, they contributed nothing to the conception. Since he had but the simplest of lenses, we can hardly be surprised that he did not discover the spermatozoa or that he did not anticipate the researches of the nineteenth century by solving the problem of fertilisation in terms of the cell theory. His discoveries were in this sense incorrect. But they still stand in the sense that they disproved, and correctly disproved, all the previous theories, and rendered untenable any model for fertilisation which involved the totality of the semen and an equivalent menstrual clot.

Harvey disproved the old ideas on fertilisation, but did he put anything in their place? What he did suggest cannot, perhaps, be dignified by the term 'theory' but he did emphasise certain aspects of the matter which seem so obvious to us that they are often passed over as being nothing novel. On the frontispiece of *De Generatione* is a picture of Jove holding an open egg in his hand. From this egg emerge many different animals, and on it is written '*Ex Ova Omnia*'. This dictum, as we have seen, has always been associated with Harvey's name, although the actual dictum does not appear in the text. Within the text, however, somewhat similar statements occur again and again, and the idea is fully discussed in 'Exercise 62—An egg is the common origin of all animals' and in 'Exercise 63—Of the generation of viviparous animals'. In the first of these Harvey discusses Aristotle's division of the sexually generated animals into three groups—the vermiparous, the oviparous and the viviparous. He disagrees with Aristotle concerning the first group, which had contained the insects. These, Harvey insists, are really oviparous. Like Fabricius before him, Harvey claims that there is virtually no difference between the insects and other groups such as the fishes, mollusca and crustacea, which even Aristotle had allowed were oviparous; and he upholds Fabricius' classification of all animals into oviparous and viviparous, as against Aristotle's threefold one. In the next 'exercise' Harvey goes further and disagrees with Fabricius' distinction. He claims that his work on deer will show that this distinction cannot be maintained, and that the 'conception', although retained in the uterus, is in every way analogous to an egg.

> Further the definition of an egg as given by Aristotle, is perfectly applicable to a conception's—'An egg', he says 'is that, the principal part of which goes to constitute an animal, the remainder to nourish the animal so constituted. Now the same thing is common to a conception, as shall be made to appear visible from the dissection of viviparous animals.
>
> Moreover as the chick is excluded from the egg under the influence of warmth derived from the incubating hen or obtained in any other way, even so is the foetus produced from the conception in the uterus under the genial warmth of the mother's body. . . . The eggs of fishes, however, increase through nourishment obtained from without; and insects and crustaceous and molluscous animals have eggs that enlarge after their extrusion. Yet are these not called eggs the less on this account, nor, indeed

are they therefore less eggs. In like manner the conception is appropriately designated by the name of ovum or egg although it requires and procures from without the variety of aliment that is needful to its growth.
(*38*, b, Ex. 63, p. 464)

Harvey presses the similarity between the conception and the egg in many passages such as this:

Now we, at the very outset of our observations, assert that *all* animals were in some sort produced from eggs. For even on the same grounds, and in the same manner and order in which a chick is engendered and developed from an egg, is the embryo of viviparous animals engendered from a pre-existing conception. Generation in both is one and identical in kind; the origin of either is from an egg or at least something that by analogy is held to be so. An egg is, as already said, a conception exposed beyond the body of the parent, whence the embryo is produced; a conception is an egg remaining within the body of the parent until the foetus has acquired the requisite perfection; in everything else they agree; they are both primordially vegetables, potentially they are animals. Wherefore the same theorems and conclusions, though they may appear paradoxical, which we drew from the history of the egg, turn out to be equally true with regard to the generation of animals generally. For it is an admitted fact that all embryos, even those of man, are procreated from some primordium or conception. Let us, therefore, say that that which is called a primordium among things arising spontaneously, and seed among plants is an egg among oviparous animals, i.e. a certain corporeal substance, from which through the motions and efficacy of an internal principle, a plant or animal of one description or another is produced; but the prime conception of viviparous animals is of the same precise nature, a fact which we have found approved both by sense and reason.
(*38*, b, Ex. 63, p. 462)

What is at first remarkable about passages like the above is the clarity with which Harvey sees through the superficial differences between the various types of sexual reproduction to an underlying unity. However, although Aristotle had used the various differences as a basis for the classification of animals, he had also insisted on a basic similarity in all sexual reproduction. So, at first sight, Harvey does not seem to be adding much to Aristotle's ideas. This is probably why many writers have tended to agree with Whitman, who maintained that Harvey's talk about the origin of all animals from eggs amounted to no more than

. . . a vague generalisation, exceeding in no way what Aristotle had already maintained.
(*96*, a, p. 217)

But this is to overlook the important difference between Harvey's theories and those of all other writers, including Aristotle. It is to miss completely the true force of Harvey's discoveries. As we have seen, all ancient theories affirmed that the hen egg was produced within the uterus from the male semen and the female secretion or menstrual blood. In so far as the mammalian embryo was held to be egg-like, it was the embryo at a later stage, after the initial period of formation, that was so regarded. For all Harvey's predecessors, physicians and Aristotelians alike, the egg was a secondary product, whose origin was to be understood in terms of their respective theories, based on the human model, of fertilisation and early development. For Harvey this is not so—the egg is no secondary production, but literally the product of fertilisation. It is not produced by any commingling of bulky secretions but is itself the initial primordium.

Hence, with his insistence on the egg as the origin of all living things, Harvey is advancing two new views: firstly, that the initial stage of the new individual is always something discrete and independent, produced by the female after intercourse; and, secondly, that the state of affairs described by him in the case of the hen is the typical or paradigm case of generation. He is, therefore, arguing that all generation, including mammalian and human, should be viewed as special cases of the more general type which is examplified by the hen. This is the exact reverse of all the previous theories, in which oviparous generation was understood in terms of the supposedly more typical and perfect viviparous generation.

The force of these suggestions depends on the meaning given by Harvey to the term 'egg' or 'ovum'. For Aristotle the word had a perfectly straightforward use. It was used to describe the object produced by the hen and similar objects produced by fishes, molluscs, etc., which, even if they lacked hard shells, were similar in appearance. Aristotle described the mammalian embryo as egg-like at the stage when the minute foetus looks egg-like, being enclosed in membranes. Harvey, too, sometimes uses the word in this ordinary descriptive sense, but there is in his work the beginnings of a more technical use. It is in this latter sense that Harvey wishes to assert that all animals are produced from 'ova'. (I shall use 'ovum' for 'egg' in this sense.) But since Harvey is a pioneer, and is working in a very difficult subject, he is by no means clear about the technical meaning he wishes to assign to the word 'ovum'. For modern biologists the ovum is defined within the cell theory and the word refers to a precise morphological (or cytological) unit. Harvey's ovum is connected with this modern concept. Harvey thinks of it as produced by the female and having the power to develop, after intercourse, into the new individual. Although he denies that the semen makes actual contact with the ovum, he insists that it is the semen which imparts to it the capacity for full development. (See the discussion of the power of the hen; *38*, b, Exs. 40 and 41, pp. 317–19.) Hence the fertile 'ovum' or 'primordium' 'derives its origin from the intercourse of the male and female and possesses the virtue of both'. The term 'primordium' is often used by Harvey as an alternative to the word 'ovum' and really gives his sense better than the latter. Since he describes as ova such very different objects as seeds, eggs and conceptions, and identifies them as ova at obviously different stages of development, it is clear that he is not thinking of the ovum in any precise anatomical terms. Like our term 'embryo' it covers a number of stages of development—in fact all stages up to that of an unequivocal plant, bird or animal. Harvey insists that the 'ovum' has within itself the power of development, and this idea, to which we will return later, constitutes one of his biggest breaks with the Aristotelian tradition.

Although Harvey returns to discuss his idea of the ovum again and again, it is difficult to find one continuous passage which gives a complete account of his view. One of the better summaries is perhaps the following, which is actually from a supplement to *De Generatione*.

> In the production of all living creatures, as I have before said, this invariably holds, that they derive their origin from a certain primary something or primordium which contains within itself both the 'matter' and the 'efficient cause'; and so is, in fact, the matter out of which, and that by which, whatsoever is produced is made. Such a primary something in animals (whether they spring from parents or arise spontaneously or from putrefaction) is a moisture enclosed in some membrane or shell; a similar body, in fact, having life within itself either actually or potentially; and this, if it is generated within an animal and remains there, until it produces an univocal (not equivocal) animal, is commonly called a 'conception'; but if it is exposed to the air by birth, or assumes its beginning under other circum-

stances (than within an animal), it is then denominated an 'egg' or 'worm'. I think, however, that in either case the word 'primordium' should be used to express that from whence the animal is formed; just as plants owe their origins to seed; all these 'primordia' have one common property—that of vitality.
(*38*, c, p. 554)

Harvey's observations included not only the initial stages of development but also the later ones. The details of these observations are of importance to the history of embryology but do not concern us. (See also *54*, pp. 133 and 145.) His general ideas on development, however, are intimately connected with his idea of the ovum, and are of importance to anyone tracing the evolution of our modern outlook on generation.

Aristotle's views on development and differentiation followed from his view on fertilisation. Assuming that in any ordinary case there was matter of a menstrual origin in the uterus, Aristotle went on to assume that the male modelled or moulded this material into a form like itself. Usually the instrument was the semen but Aristotle also believed that it was possible for the male of certain animals (e.g. the insects) to dispense with this instrument and to act directly on the female 'matter'. Differentiation was, for him, produced by the male in this already available material, and once the initial organs were produced they increased or grew, fed by the supplementary food. Hence the distinction between the matter out of which the organism was formed and the food to be used later. The model for this form of initial development was the sculptor acting on the stone or wood to produce the ultimate piece of statuary. This idea of development fitted in with his general scheme for all nature and enabled him to explain generation in terms of his general theory of four types of 'cause'. Likewise, the physicians also believed that the embryo was formed from the two commingled secretions which, for them too, provided the matter which was to differentiate out into the actual new organism. Here again, if they were atomists, it was possible to explain development in terms of these fundamental particles as Lucretius had done. Thus both these theories accounted for the gradual appearance of the organs in terms of an initial differentiation followed by growth. Both gave accounts of generation which rendered it explicable in terms of their more general explanatory systems.

Harvey's investigations led him to reject both theories, and his concept of an initial minute primordium made another account of development essential. In order to express his ideas Harvey introduced a new term—'epigenesis'. All animals which are formed from ova or primordia develop epigenetically.

> . . . and this happens to all those that are born from an egg (i.e. ovum). As in these the process of growth and formation are carried on at the same time, and a separation and distinction of the parts takes place in a regularly observed order, so in this case there is no immediate pre-existing material present, for the incorporation of the foetus, but as soon as ever the material is created and prepared, so soon are growth and form commenced; the nutriment is immediately accompanied by the presence of that which it has to feed.
> (*38*, b, Ex. 45, p. 338)

Thus, Harvey's account of development is of a simultaneous process of growth and differentiation. His model is not the sculptor but the potter who forms his pot by adding material to it and shaping it at the same time. But he insists that the primordium itself is responsible. Unlike Aristotle, who had an analogue for the sculptor in the semen, Harvey has no analogue for the potter. Epigenesis is therefore introduced purely as a descriptive term—to describe but not to account for the observed facts.

To this process of epigenesis Harvey opposes the process of metamorphosis.

> In generation by metamorphosis, forms are created as if by the impression of a seal, or as if they were adjusted in a mould; in truth the whole material is transformed.
> (*38*, b, Ex. 45, p. 335)

The model for this is that of the mould in which the object is produced from material present at the beginning of the process, without any additions. In such a way, according to Harvey, is the butterfly produced from the pupa. In assessing this suggestion it must be remembered that whereas modern biologists speak of the grub, the pupa and the adult as stages in the life cycle of one individual butterfly, Harvey and his contemporaries always regarded the grub as one individual and the butterfly as another. The latter was thus considered a new organism generated within the pupa or aurelia. Since the case did not increase in size, nor take in any new matter, the butterfly must be formed from the material present, therefore it must be an example of generation by metamorphosis.

Harvey's work had led him to disagree with his predecessors on the facts of fertilisation, to introduce the idea of the ovum and to give a new account of the process of development. He had certainly done much to overthrow the previous theories. But his work raised a host of new and extremely difficult problems. The theories by which the ancients explained the assumed facts were readily plausible, for they tied in, as we saw, with their general schemata of explanation. Harvey could do little in this respect. He described the phenomenon with great clarity and vigour in many passages like the following:

> It is just as if the whole chick were created by a command to this effect by the Divine Architect: 'let there be a similar colourless mass, and let it be divided into parts and made to increase, and in the meanwhile, while it is growing let there be a separation and delineation of the parts; and let this part be tender and denser and more glistening, that be softer and more coloured.' And it was so. Now it is in this very manner that the structure of the chick in the egg goes on day by day; all its parts are formed, nourished and augmented out of the same material.
> (*38*, b, Ex. 45, p. 339)

But when it came to offering an explanation Harvey had to confess himself at a standstill.

The explanations offered by both the physicians and Aristotle depended, as we have seen, on there being a mass in the uterus immediately after conception. Since Harvey had demonstrated that there was no such mass their detailed explanations were, of course, untenable. But Harvey was prepared to go further, and to claim that neither type of explanation was adequate for the facts which he had observed.

Before considering Harvey's arguments in detail it is necessary to say something of Harvey's attitude to biological explanation. Harvey was recognised by his contemporaries not only as a great scientist but also as a pioneer of the new methods. Professor Passmore has pointed out (see *61*) that when Hobbes dedicated his *Elements of Philosophy* to his predecessors he named Harvey amongst such men as Kepler, Galileo, Gassendi and Mersenne and that Harvey alone shared with Galileo the honour of being mentioned in this way by Descartes in his *Discourses on Method*. Harvey was one of the greatest exponents of

the empirical trend in the seventeenth century. Not only was he a great experimenter and careful observer but he was prepared to accept as fact nothing which was not established by these means.
A sparing theorist, he claimed:

> I own that I am of the opinion that one's first duty is to enquire whether the thing be or not, before asking wherefore it is.
> (*38*, a, p. 122)

The circulation of the blood was for Harvey a theory, since he could not see the capillaries which connect the arteries and veins. But this theory was backed by numerous experiments and calculations so that he could rightly say:

> I have not endeavoured from causes and probable principles to demonstrate my propositions, but as of higher authority, to establish them by appeals to sense and experiment after the manner of the anatomists.
> (*38*, a, p. 134)

Though he obviously would not rule out the use of reason or imagination in framing hypotheses, it is clear that he would only accept those which led to testable consequences. In this connection he quoted with approval Aristotle's remark that:

> Faith is to be given to reason if the things which are demonstrated agree with these which are perceived by sense: when things have been thoroughly scrutinized, then are the senses to be trusted rather than the reason.
> (*38*, a, p. 131)

and it was in accordance with such principles that he rejected both Descartes' view that the heart action was due to heat and the idea that the blood was animated by an incorporeal 'spirit'.

When he criticised the types of explanation previously offered for generation he again applied these same rigorous standards. The atomistic type of explanation would not do because:

> There is a greater and more divine mystery in the generation of animals than the simple collecting together, alteration and composition of a whole out of the parts would seem to imply; in as much as here the whole has a separate constitution and existence before its parts, the mixture before the elements.
> (*38*, b, Ex. 46, p. 340)

Given the state of both chemistry and biology at the time that was written he was right: no such hypothesis could be tested by observation or experiment. Harvey preferred to leave the matter unexplained rather than to indulge in sheer speculation.

Harvey considered in greater detail the type of explanation offered by Aristotle and his followers which was, of course, the one most generally accepted in his day; and because of its importance he devoted many sections (particularly, *38*, b, Exs. 44 and 50) to this subject. Perhaps this is one of the chief reasons why modern historians have sometimes accused him of being an Aristotelian. But Harvey's conclusions certainly do not support this view for he, in fact, disagreed with Aristotle on all the important issues. First, he pointed out that Aristotle himself was extremely inconsistent when he tried to apply the idea of an efficient cause to generation, and that he had mentioned a number of additional causes, such as coagulation and motion, before he finally spoke of the semen itself as a cause. According to Harvey, the whole idea of an 'efficient cause' was inapplicable to this type of phenomena for it was, for Aristotle, essentially an external agent. Thus, when Aristotle spoke of the semen as the efficient cause, he was thinking of it as acting on the matter from the outside. But even in Aristotle's view of the origin of a foetus, the semen could not be thought of as present throughout the lifetime of the new organism. So Aristotle had further assumed that the semen engendered a soul (anima or entelechy) in the new organism. But how the semen engendered the soul, Aristotle did not explain. So, said Harvey, this explanation simply replaced the original mystery by another in every way similar to the first but couched in more bewildering language. To ask how the semen engendered the soul is to ask again for an explanation of generation in more metaphysical language.

In other contexts, Aristotle had spoken of the soul as the cause of differentiation and growth. Harvey had always been opposed to such explanations and had bitterly attacked this use of 'spirits' or 'anima' in his previous works (*38*, a, pp. 116–19). He again pointed out the ambiguities contained in all references to 'spirits'. If the 'spirit' is to be thought of as distinct from the body then there is absolutely no evidence for such a theory. If, on the other hand, by spirit is simply meant the essential nature of the living parts, then this is merely to describe what happens but not to explain. Finally, Harvey summed up his views on Aristotle's explanations as follows:

Wherefore it is no wonder that the most excellent philosopher was in perplexity on this head, and that he admitted so great a variety of efficient causes, and at one time has been compelled to resort to automations, coagulations, art, instruments and motions for illustrations; at another time to an 'anima' in the egg and in the seed of the male. Moreover, when he seems positively and definitely to determine what it is in each seed, whether of plants or animals, which render the same fertile, he repudiates heat and force as improper agents; nor does he admit any faculty of a similar quality; nor can he find anything in the seed which shall be fit for that office; but he is driven to acknowledge something incorporeal, and coming from foreign sources, which he supposes (like art or the mind) to form the foetus with intelligence and foresight, and to institute and ordain all the parts for its welfare. He takes refuge, I say, in a thing which is not recognisable by us; namely, in a spirit contained in the seed, and in a frothy body, and in the nature of that spirit, corresponding in proportion to the elements of the stars. But what this is he has nowhere informed us.
(*38*, b, Ex. 47, pp. 349–50)

But, while Harvey could see that previous explanations of the differentiation and organisation of each new living thing were inadequate, he could only contribute two positive ideas to this aspect of generation. He insisted, as we have seen, that all living things started from a vital primordium which he termed the ovum, and that there was nothing to suggest that this was moulded or formed by any external agent like the semen or the uterus. Secondly, he insisted that this ovum slowly turned, through orderly stages, into the appropriate adult: again there seemed to be no apparent external cause. He could see the difficulty involved in any explanation of this in terms of physical and inorganic forces, which seemed inadequate to explain such foresight. On the other hand, he had no place for the type of explanation which involved a controlling mind or soul. He did suggest that the whole must exist 'in potentia' within the ovum, since otherwise its subsequent development seemed quite incomprehensible, but he was quite aware that by saying this he was explaining nothing.

As we have seen, Harvey's determination to rely on his observations had led him to deny a material contact between the semen and the ovum. Here, of course, the best of methodological principles led to a factual error and so it is little wonder that he was forced to say:

. . . for my part I think there is more to admire and marvel at in conception. It is a matter, in truth, full of obscurity.
(*38*, d, p. 575)

In the course of his discussions on the subject he made many shrewd observations on the general effects of the male upon the female. For example, he pointed out that the behaviour and physical characteristics of caged female animals change if a cage containing males is brought into their vicinity, and that a spinster will alter both physically and psychologically after marriage, even if she does not become pregnant. He suggested that conception itself might be like magnetisation, or like the conception of an idea, or like a contagion which can be spread without any apparent material contact. But he was well aware that these analogies did 'but replace one mystery with another'. His final words on the subject not only show his despair of explaining fertilisation, but also his more general despair of finding a suitable model for the explanation of biological phenomena:

. . . if I say this contagion is not of the nature of any corporeal substance, it follows of necessity that it is incorporeal. And if, on further enquiry, it should appear that it is neither spirit, nor demon nor soul, nor any part of a soul, nor anything having a soul, as I believe can be proved by various arguments and experiments, what remains, since I am myself unable to conjecture anything besides, nor has anyone imagined aught else even in his dreams, but to confess myself at a standstill?
(*38*, d, p. 581)

Harvey's previous works had provoked much adverse criticism but *De Generatione* was accepted without any storms. This was due partly to Harvey's personal prestige: in the period between 1628 when *De Motu* was published and 1651 when this work appeared, more and more people had come to accept Harvey's views on the circulation of the blood. The older opponents had died and the younger men admired his work, so that Harvey, in his later years, was the most respected and revered physiologist in Europe.

But the more favourable reception of *De Generatione* was also due to a complete change in the intellectual climate of the times. As we have seen, Harvey himself had done much to produce that change; but by 1651 the change was almost complete. The whole Aristotelian framework had crumpled and a new outlook had been accepted.

The old ideas had suffered a two-pronged attack. Their presuppositions had been examined and had been shown to be unnecessarily cumbersome while, at the same time, the factual support for these had been examined in detail and had been found either to be incorrect or to be in need of drastic amplification. Although the emphasis varied in the different cases, all the works of Galileo, Gassendi, Descartes, Harvey and Marsenne followed this pattern. *De Generatione* which appears a difficult and diffuse book to us was, in fact, one of the last books of this type.

To contemporary readers it obviously appeared as a straightforward work whose general approach was by now familiar. It differed from some of the other works of this type because Harvey, unlike some of his contemporaries, was always extremely polite about his predecessors and in fact Dr Ent in his preface to the work commented on this:

> 'And we have evidence of his singular candour in this, that he never hostilely attacks any previous writer, but ever courteously sets down and comments upon the opinions of each: and indeed he is wont to say that it is argument of an indifferent cause when it is contested with violence and distemper: and that truth scarce wants an advocate.'
> (*38*, Preface, p. 151)

Certainly the book gave support to the new attitude: here was yet another field in which careful enquiry and observation had shown the previous ideas to be ill-founded. If the work met with less criticism, it nevertheless was widely read and, as we shall see in the next chapter, it had an enormous effect on the subsequent work done in the subject. It is perfectly in accord with this contemporary opinion of *De Generatione* that the original statue of Harvey at the Royal College of Physicians (which perished in the fire of 1666) should have linked his two great interests together and have paid them almost equal respect, claiming that

> he who gave motion to the blood even as he allotted to animals their origin, has deserved to stand here for ever as their tutelary deity.
> (*54*, p. 151, footnote)

3

The Initial Stages of the Preformation Theory

'If the egg consists of homogeneous matter as is presumed on this hypothesis [epigenesis], it can only develop into a foetus by a miracle, which would surpass every other phenomenon in the world.'

C. Perrault, ESSAIS DE PHYSICQUE, 1680

HARVEY, as we saw in the last chapter, had asserted that all living things start as vital primordia or ova and that mammalian reproduction was to be understood as analogous to the oviparous type exhibited by the hen. But while he could trace the origin of the yolk (bearing the vital cicatricula) back to the ovary in the fowl he could find no equivalent point of origin for the mammalian ovum or 'conception'. As far as he could see, this conception appeared, after a considerable delay, free within the body of the uterus. But if his analogy with the fowl was to have much force it was clear that there should be a mammalian organ comparable to the fowl's ovary. Harvey himself examined the 'female testicles' but could see no changes in them either prior to or immediately following copulation. Being committed to his idea of confirmation by visual inspection, he concluded that they played no part in the reproductive process.

The so-called 'female testicles' had been recognised from the earliest times and had been named as a result of comparative studies between the anatomy of the sexes in various mammals including man. Most sixteenth century anatomists had described these structures but their function had always been obscure. Vesalius and others had actually seen the parts we call the Graafian follicles, but had believed them to be the result of an infection and had therefore named them 'hydatid vesicles'. Immediately after the appearance of Harvey's *De Generatione*, increased attention was paid to these organs. As early as 1656 Wharton (*94*, Chap. 33) suggested that if, as Harvey claimed, the semen could not be found in the mammalian uterus, this was because it passed up the Fallopian tubes to the female testicles, where it intermingled with a female secretion and returned to the uterus as the recognisable conception. In 1667 Steno (*75*) asserted that the female testicles in mammals should not be viewed as the equivalent of the male organs but as comparable with the ovaries of all types of oviparous animals including those of the fishes (on which he was working), and that they should be called by the same name. He was, therefore, the first to grasp the implication of Harvey's analogy and to apply it fully to the mammalian case. But at this period he was unable to give his assertion the necessary factual backing and, since his work on the subject did not appear until 1675, he was anticipated by de Graaf. In 1668 Van Horne (*84*) suggested that the hydatid vesicles were indeed the ova, an idea which was reinforced by Kerckring's suggestion, made by 1671 (*41*), that the ovaries in the viviparous must be the source of the 'eggs' just as they are in the fowl. Thus Harvey's incomplete analogy was being pressed further and the climate of opinion was already prepared for de Graaf's confirmatory work.

In 1672 de Graaf published his *De mulierum organis generationi inservientibus* (*17*). In this work he described how he had dissected rabbits at varying intervals after coition and how, with the aid of lenses, he had examined both the ovaries and uterus. He showed that the ovaries did change during the lifetime of the animals, and that these changes were connected with the waxing and waning of fertility. The 'hydatid vesicles' were present in all fertile animals, so they were not, as Vesalius had imagined, an infection, but a genuine part of the organ. Moreover, after coition, some of these vesicles (= Graafian follicles) appeared to lose their contents and only a scar remained. Generally, in pregnant animals, the number of recent scars corresponds to the number of embryos in the uterus. In rabbits he could find the first traces of the 'conceptions' (in Harvey's sense) in the uterus three days after intercourse, whereas the follicles appeared to be empty about twenty hours earlier. With the means at his disposal, de Graaf could identify nothing resembling an egg within the follicles. Since the 'conception', when it first appeared, was smaller than the scar left in the ovary, he was inclined to believe that, after intercourse, 'something' must be released by the follicles and that this 'something' must travel down the tubes into the uterus, where it appeared as the 'conception'. Since he could find no trace of the semen in the uterus or beyond, he thought it possible that fertilisation did not involve any material contact between the semen and the product of the ovaries. But since all changes seemed to follow copulation, he also believed that the male must act upon the ova while they are still within the ovary.

De Graaf's work was soon confirmed by other investigators, some of whom had obviously started their enquiries before de Graaf's book was published. Swammerdam in 1672 (*78*), Steno in 1675 (*76*), and Bartholinus in 1678 (*4*), all confirmed the existence of the follicles in different mammalian ovaries, and the connection between these structures and subsequent appearance of the embryos. Thus Harvey's doctrine of the origins of all animals from eggs now had added meaning and the analogy between oviparous and viviparous modes of reproduction was more clearly understood.

This confirmation of Harvey's discoveries really created a difficult situation within the study of generation. But in order to understand just why this was so it is necessary to digress and consider the outlook of the times. Very generally, it might be said that for many centuries all biological thought had been vitalistic. Both Aristotle and Galen had accounted for all vital activity, including generation, by supposing it to be controlled by 'souls' or 'faculties'. True, both authors had also supposed that some of the processes could be understood by analogy with non-vital processes, but such explanations were only used in a somewhat limited way. Moreover, since the whole of western civilisation had more or less accepted the Aristotelian description of the material world, and had amalgamated this with Christian theology, these vitalistic explanations tied in with the general framework. In such a situation, the explanations of generation offered by both schools no doubt seemed satisfactory enough, especially as both could fall back on their belief in an initial mass of matter within the uterus, as the material out of which the actual body was formed.

Harvey's work on generation appeared just as this Aristotelian outlook had been destroyed. By 1651, the majority of European scholars had accepted the view that scientific explanations should dispense with such concepts as 'final cause' and 'spirit', and should concentrate on physical causes such as motion and impact. Indeed most of the *avant-garde* were fast moving towards the purely mechanistic and even atomistic approach which was to be so characteristic of the next hundred years.

It is, of course, impossible to assign any exact date to such intellectual movements. In the field of generation itself, some works which appeared after the middle of the seventeenth century were written by people whose outlook was completely Aristotelian (for example Faber—*De Generatione Animalium*, 1666), but these were ignored by most other workers and made little impression on the opinion of the time. Likewise a group of advanced thinkers—notably Highmore (40 *A*) whose work appeared just after Harvey's, Descartes (died 1650) and Gassendi (30) (died 1655) who had turned their attention to generation just before Harvey's work was published had all returned in various ways to the corpuscular theories of the Greek atomists. They all assumed that the new organism was actually formed from a mass of particles which must be present in the uterus. In a sense these writers were obviously moving in the right direction, but, as Harvey's investigations showed, they were wrong in thinking that the mass of particles provided the gross matter out of which the embryo was formed. It so happened that, although these works were written before Harvey's book was published, they appeared after it. When they did appear they were ignored or viewed with disfavour, probably because of their erroneous assumptions, but also perhaps because their explanations seemed too speculative. These theories are interesting and will be considered later, but since they made so little impression on the seventeenth century outlook, they may be ignored for the present.

As we have seen already, Harvey's works tended to stress the importance of observation and experiment, an increased emphasis on which was a vital part of that change in outlook which is sometimes called the scientific revolution. Another aspect of this change was the demand, already mentioned, for a new type of explanation. In physics, these two aspects could be linked; the empirical discoveries tended to make a new form of explanation necessary, while at the same time explanations in the new form paved the way for further discoveries. It was because the two aspects worked together so well in this field, and gave such promise of success, that the change was accepted even before Newton's *Principia* was published. But in the biological enquiries there was no such happy linkage—the more carefully the facts were studied, the more remote must have seemed the possibility of explaining them in the required manner. The dilemma was particularly clear in the case of generation. Here Harvey had given a brilliant description of the wonder he felt as he watched the process of development. Yet despite all his work on the subject he was unable to suggest an explanatory theory to account for the facts. In the subsequent period the position grew worse: the new emphasis on observation resulted in the discovery of more inexplicable facts, but at the same time the old type of explanation, in terms of vital principles, became more unfashionable. Atomistic explanations gave promise of success within the physical sciences, but in the field of generation these seemed too speculative and abstract.

Before returning to the history of the subject, a summary of the above argument may help to emphasise the difficulties which faced anyone attempting to account for generation in the mid-seventeenth century:

1 The discovery that the new organism did not arise from a mass of material donated by both parents had undermined all the ancient theories.

2 The explanations offered by Aristotle had been rejected. Moreover, all such vitalistic explanations were unfashionable, so that any return to a modification of this type of explanation was not likely to meet with success.

3 The empirical aspect of the scientific revolution, emphasised by Harvey himself, stressed both the need for careful observation of facts, and the need for theories to accord in detail with all facts obtained in this way. Here the facts were such that any corpuscular explanation must have seemed too speculative.

4 The facts of embryo development, vividly described by Harvey and later by Malpighi, could not be overlooked; but they were very difficult to fit in to any simple mechanistic view of a sort that could be imagined within the seventeenth century framework.

It was just at this period, as Harvey's work was being confirmed and extended, that the preformation theory made its first appearance. Harvey had merely claimed that the ovum must be potentially an animal, but it was now suggested that in fact the predelineations of all the organs must be present at this stage. It was assumed that the gradual appearance and apparent creation of the parts observed, as the ovum turned into the embryo and then into the adult, were simply due to an increase, in size and in hardness, of parts that were already present.

Needham (*54*, pp. 66, 121 and 169) and Cole (*11*, pp. 37 ff.) have pointed out that this theory was not new but, in fact, had 'its roots in antiquity'. Certainly, the idea that the semen is analogous to seed is very ancient, and since the seed had obvious parts, this would tend to give rise to the idea that the parts were also present at the commencement of animal generation. It was this aspect which Joseph of Aromataria (*3*) emphasised in a famous letter written in 1625. In this he gave it as his opinion that, just as the form of the plant is visible in the seeds and in bulbs, so might the chick be present in the egg before incubation. This letter aroused little interest when it was first published but, after preformation had been accepted, it was reprinted in several journals. On the whole, apart from a very rare reference to the past, the preformationists seemed to be unaware of the fact that their theory was not a completely new creation. Indeed, when this letter of Joseph's was reprinted in the Transactions of the Royal Society in 1694 (*3*), it was accompanied by a short introduction which expressed surprise that the idea had occurred as early as 1625.

But from the point of view of the seventeenth century it was not enough to claim that the parts were preformed within the ovum. It was no easier to imagine how they might be suddenly precipitated out at this stage, than to account for their gradual appearance during the subsequent period. The preformation of any individual ovum would account for the gradual appearance of the parts in that particular case and would also explain how an apparently unformed mass could act as a completely independent organism. But it simply shifted the problem of the origin of organised living matter back one stage further, to the origin of the preformed germ itself. Since the major problem was how differentiated parts could ever form from unorganised matter, the seventeenth century preformationists assumed, in addition, that all the living things there were to be, had in fact been organised by God at creation, and that encapsulated within the first parent all future generations were present. The first female of every species, therefore, contained within herself all future generations of her kind. Each generation in turn would come to maturity, and when all the created germs had reached the adult form the species would become extinct. This latter view was later known as *emboîtement*, and it was preformation with *emboîtement* which constituted the true preformation theory. It followed from such a view that there was no true generation; what appeared as the formation of a new individual was simply the growth of an organised living thing which had been formed at the beginning of Time.

It was Swammerdam who first introduced the theory into scientific literature, when he mentioned it in a book on insects published in 1669 (*77*). In 1672 he gave a more complete account of it in a work on reproduction, but the theory had apparently had some currency before it appeared in print (*78*). Swammerdam himself reported that he had discussed the idea with a group in Paris in 1668, and also mentioned that when he first proposed his theory it was already held by one of his learned friends. According to Cole, this friend is usually believed to be the philosopher, Malebranche, who discussed the theory in his book *De la recherche de la vérité*, which appeared in 1674. (See also *11*, pp. 41–51.)

In spite of the obvious difficulties and absurdities of this theory, it won immediate support, and continued to dominate most of the work done in this branch of biology for over a hundred and fifty years. Moreover, it was accepted in slightly varying forms by such great naturalists as Leeuwenhoek, Ray, Réaumur, Haller, Spallanzani, Bonnet and even Cuvier. It is impossible to believe that men of this calibre should have all been deluded into accepting a theory such as this, unless they felt there were some very good reasons for doing so.

It is already clear that, at the time preformation was first suggested, the study of sexual generation was in a somewhat unusual position, in that it was completely without any explanatory theory. In such a situation one would expect the announcement of any new theory to provoke interest, and one might also expect that for a short time it would gain adherents with relative ease. Moreover, this particular theory accorded quite well with the general outlook of the period. Individual development and differentiation were reduced to growth, which could be regarded as a more or less purely mechanical process. Although the theory denied that living things could be formed from inorganic matter, this view did not include any assumptions about vitalistic forces or spirits acting in a mysterious way within living organisms. God had created all individuals at the beginning, just as he had created all other parts of the Universe. The model of the machine, created by God, but working according to relatively simple physical laws, had been extended to include all living things.

A theory gains in plausibility if it accords with the current world picture; but it cannot even be considered unless it is in accordance with recognised principles within its own field. Preformation was completely in accord with the central biological assumption of the time, and brought the only aberrant case within this assumption. This central assumption might be described as the law that animals function because they have organs, for it assumed that all animals have organs, and that their essential vital activities were always associated with the appropriate organs. Seventeenth century naturalists know enough about comparative anatomy to know that equivalent organs could differ in form, e.g. that both lungs and gills could perhaps serve as respiratory organs, that digestive systems could differ vastly in structure, and that the reproductive organs did not always consist of exactly the same parts. But no animals they had examined lacked organs and, although little was known about the physiological processes, what was known tended to stress this association—for in all cases where an organ was injured or destroyed it seemed that the associated function ceased or was impaired. The law therefore seemed to rest on the best inductive evidence. Indeed, it might have been extended to include all living things; for the familiar plants could be seen to have parts which were regarded as equivalent to organs. Very little was known of plant physiology, so that any attempt to assign functions to the leaves, stem, flower and roots had to be conjectural but the problems were always posed in this form. This 'law' was, of course, no new idea: Aristotle both implied his belief in it, and also formulated it, in various different ways. In one place, when engaged in a general discussion on the nature of life, he says:

> The soul may therefore be defined as the first actuality of a natural body . . . and the body must be of a kind which possesses organs. (In plants also the parts are their organs, very simple ones, such as the leaf which covers the pod, and the pod which covers the seed, but the roots are analogous to the mouth, for both these absorb food.)
> (2)

But to suggest that the seventeenth century acceptance of the principle was due to any direct regard for Aristotle's authority is wrong. It was accepted by everyone, including Aristotle, because it seemed so obviously true.

In order to understand anything of the subsequent history of generation it is necessary both to see how deeply this assumption was embedded and how strongly it was backed by empirical evidence. It does not do simply to say that at this period they lacked the cell theory

—for this suggests that they lacked any general ideas, and were merely making these random observations which were to be assembled to form the basis of a nineteenth century science. It is doubtful if any continuous enquiry could have been maintained had this been the case, or if the nineteenth century achievements would have been possible against such a background. As we shall see, the fact that their central assumption was wrong often made their task more difficult, and led them to hold positions which would be otherwise inexplicable. Yet at the same time they lacked the evidence and the means to obtain the evidence, which could have reasonably caused them to alter this assumption.

The only observations which were not in accordance with this central idea were those made on young embryos. Harvey had claimed that from the moment it became visible the primordium acted as a living unit, but he could see no trace of organs, within what appeared to be a homogeneous mass. For seventeenth century biologists these observations must have seemed almost self-contradictory. It was as though some biologist today were to claim that he had discovered objects which exhibited the living characteristics but appeared to be composed of simple chemical compounds and contained no complicated proteins and no nucleic acids. The preformation theory solved this dilemma, for, according to the theory, the primordium did, in fact, possess the parts essential for life, and the case could then be assimilated into the general pattern.

Thus it is possible to account for the attention paid to the idea of preformation. There was a need for a new conceptual scheme: the preformationist scheme fitted in fairly well with the main world view, and it brought an apparent exception within the general biological framework of the time. These facts alone might have assured its success. But there were also two kinds of new evidence which seemed to give it indirect support. Both were connected with the more common use of the microscope, which, though it was still very inefficient, did reveal a new world of living things and totally unexpected aspects of familiar animals and plants.

The first type of evidence concerned the discovery of microscopic forms of life in pond water and infusions. Although it was impossible to see any details within these creatures, they were naturally assumed to conform to the general rule and to possess organs. Leeuwenhoek, in a letter written to the elder Huygens, calculated the probable size of the blood vessels and muscles in the smallest animals (probably bacteria) which he had observed in an infusion of ginger (*25*, p. 187). The general impression created by these studies might be summarised by the slogan 'Size is only relative'. It is perhaps worth noting that the discovery of microscopic life followed immediately after the recognition that the universe was also much bigger than mediaeval scientists had believed possible. Thus imagination was dazzled simultaneously by the infinitely big as well as by the infinitely small. This, of course, played into the hands of the preformationists, for it was evidence that the extreme minuteness of the preformed individuals of the future generations, which the theory entailed, need not be an insuperable obstacle to its acceptance.

Cole gives the following admirable summary of Malebranche's view on this point:

> Since animals of microscopic life move like others they must have legs and feet, skeletons, muscles, tendons and blood systems. We must assume this because these animals live, feed and move voluntarily from place to place. 'The imagination is lost and astonished at the sight of so strange a smallness', but 'our sight is very limited and it should not limit its object', and in this small world are found as many things, although smaller in proportion, as occur in the larger world in which we live. Perhaps these small animals have others which parasitise them, which may be imperceptible on account of their incredible smallness. What a mite is to us these animals will be to a mite. Malebranche then discusses the divisibility of matter, and considers it possible that there may be a series of animals becoming smaller and smaller to infinity, although our imagination may be scared at the thought. If, however, animals exist a thousand times smaller than a mite why should we suppose that they are the last and smallest of all? It is on the contrary more reasonable to believe that there are animals much smaller than any which have been discovered.
> (*11*, pp. 50–1)

Garden puts the point more succinctly when he says:

> It seems most probable, that the stamina of all plants and animals that have been, or ever shall be in the world, have been formed *ab origine mundi*, by the Almighty Creator within the first of each respective kind. And he who considers the nature of vision, that it does not give us the true magnitude, but the proportions of things; and that which seems to our naked eye but a point, may truly be made up of as many parts as there seem to us

to be in the whole visible world, will not think this an absurd or impossible thing.
(*29*, pp. 474–83)

The second kind of indirect evidence which seemed to support the preformation theory was also connected with the new discoveries made by the microscopists. By using hot water or alcohol to harden the parts, and then subjecting developing organisms to microscopic inspection, it was often possible to see the new parts of plants and animals long before they were visible to the naked eye. Swammerdam had been able, by this method, to make out the structure of the butterfly within the pupa and even within the worm or caterpillar. He rightly concluded that the caterpillar was not one individual, the chrysalis another, and the butterfly another; but that these were all states in one continuous life cycle. But he wrongly assumed that the butterfly had been present in the caterpillar from the beginning, and that this sort of thing was true of other animals.

From whence it follows, that in reality the Caterpillar or worm is not changed into a Nymph, nor to go a step further, the Nymph into a winged animal; but that the same worm or caterpillar, which on casting its skin assumes the form of a Nymph becomes afterwards a winged animal. Nor, indeed, can it be said that there happens any other change on this occasion than what is observed in chickens, from eggs which are not transformed into chicks or hens *but grow to be such by the expansion of parts already formed.* In the same manner the Tad-pole is not changed into a frog, but becomes a frog, by the infolding and increasing of some of its parts.
(*77* and *37*, p. 370)

The early preformationists were greatly impressed by this second argument from insect metamorphosis. Swammerdam, for instance, is said to have used it at the early meeting in Paris in 1668. When asked his opinions on generation, he replied by producing a silk-worm which he passed round the assembled company, asking them if they could see anything of the moth. When they failed, he triumphantly peeled off the outer skin, revealing the rudiments of the winged animal within.

That the preformation theory, which seems so strange to us, should have been proposed and enthusiastically accepted during the seventeenth century, no longer seems so remarkable once the actual situation within the study of generation at that time has been examined. To sum up:

An investigation cannot proceed without a theory—it will either be abandoned, or a new theory will be found.

It would not have been easy to ignore the subject of generation—it was of great intrinsic interest, and it had been a traditional enquiry on which the ancients, particularly Aristotle, had focussed attention. Harvey's book both reminded the readers of the work already done and drew attention to the inadequacies of the results. Harvey, however, left the subject without any explanatory theory.

A theory, to be acceptable, must account for the facts, but it must also accord with the overall view of nature, and with the more fundamental assumptions within the subject at the time of its proposal. If additional indirect evidence can be found to render the assumptions of the theory more plausible, this will greatly increase its acceptability. The preformation theory had all these points in its favour.

If preformation is accepted, only one sex can be regarded as the donor of the preformed germ. The early preformationalists all assumed that the preformation was in the ovum, i.e. they were ovists. This was the logical outcome of the research of the period which had, for twenty years, been emphasising the female contribution to generation. The fate and function of the semen was in doubt, and most people believed that it did not come into direct contact with the ovum, but supplied an indirect stimulus.

The preformation theory, itself, can be understood in two different ways. In the first place it may be regarded as a simple prediction of what will be seen when the germ (ovum) is examined with the aid of a good microscope. In this form it is susceptible of direct empirical verification. Since the theory was introduced in conjunction with the discussion of the visible moth in the caterpillar, it seems very likely that some of its adherents did, at first, really believe that more careful microscopic inspection of embryos would reveal traces of all the organs in the smallest primordium. There is no reason why they should not have expected this and, indeed, there seemed to be some direct evidence in its favour. In 1671 (just when preformation was first suggested), Croone deposited a paper with the Royal Society (*12*) in which he claimed to have observed the complete rudiments of the chick in an unincubated egg. He used the same technique as Swammerdam had used with insects, and placed the cicatricula and adjacent yolk into warm water. These then assumed a form which suggested a chick. It seems probable, from the drawing, that he was really looking at a piece of vitelline membrane which had happened to take this form. (Suggested by Cole, *11*, p. 47.) Croone simply stated that his experiment seemed to show that the completed chick appeared suddenly at conception, and he made no attempt to link this with the theory of preformation. The paper is interesting, however, as it shows that, at this period, the possibility of finding evidence for the corporeal existence of the chick in the ovum was definitely entertained.

But, by and large, there is good evidence to suggest that most preformationists did not accept this simple version of the theory, and did not believe that the adult organs could ever be seen in this way in the young embryo. Most preformationists would have given descriptions of embryo development which included such phrases as 'at the third day the blood is seen', 'on the fifth day the heart is visible', and the like. In fact, though they might dispute on the details, they gave and accepted descriptions which were essentially similar to those given by Aristotle or Harvey, or even a present-day embryologist (providing that the latter restricted himself to describing organs). In 1672 and 1675 Malpighi published the most accurate and well illustrated accounts of the development of the chick which had yet appeared (*51*). This increase in accuracy was achieved by using a microscope to investigate the area around the cicatricula, which was thus seen in much more detail. By this means, Malpighi was able to see the blastoderm and the gradual development of the network of vessels in this region. He described how the heart beat before the blood could be seen, how the somites developed and how the neural groove and the optic vesicles appeared. His work was mainly descriptive, and he did not discuss the causes of the process he described. Most authors, apart from Adelman (see comment in *33*, p. 46), have assumed that Malpighi was a preformationist, and there is indeed one sentence which suggests that he believed that the rudiments of the chick must be present in the egg as the parts of the plant are in the seed. However, no matter what Malpighi's own view on the matter was, the important point is that he gave a description of the gradual appearance of the parts and that his work was widely known, admired and accepted by the preformationists as additional proof for their views.

Preformationists who accepted the theory in this way obviously thought of it as an *explanatory theory*, which would account for the gradual and orderly emergence of each organ, and which would also explain how the organism could function as a living unit before some of the apparently essential organs appeared. (The organism was apparently alive before there was any sign of, for instance, a heart—an essential organ for adult life.) In this form the theory cannot be directly verified, but many obviously thought that better microscopes and methods of hardening the material would reveal the parts at an earlier stage, and the earlier the part could be seen the more pleased they would be. However, there is more than a hint, even in Swammerdam's writings, that it was not supposed that even great improvements in these methods would really render the parts visible. The best analogy is perhaps the child's 'magic' painting book: here each page appears as a black and white picture which becomes coloured by the application of water. The pictures finally have the colours red, blue, etc. because the appropriate dyes were present below the surface and appeared as the water dissolved them, but the colours cannot be seen without the addition of the water. In the same way, in this version of preformation, the ovum eventually assumed adult form because growth and hardening has rendered visible parts which were already present, but which could not be seen, no matter how good the microscope was, nor what additional techniques were employed, until these changes had started to take place.

4

The Animalculist Version of the Preformation Theory, 1683–1740

'. . . *there is another kind* [*of animalcule*] *which must have a different origin. Such, for example, are those which one discovers with the microscope in the semen of animals, which seem to belong to it, and are present in such a great quantity as to comprise almost the whole of it. They are formed of a transparent substance, their movements are very brisk and their shape is similar to that of frogs before their limbs are formed. This discovery, which was made in Holland for the first time, seems very important, and should give employment to those interested in the generation of animals.*

Letter from Christiaan Huygens dated March 26th, 1678

VERY soon after the orginal version of the preformation theory became known (about 1671) a new discovery was made which changed the entire position. Microscopes had become slightly more common and it was inevitable that, within a short time, a microscopic examination of the semen of man or of some of the higher animals should be made. Leeuwenhoek was probably the first to conduct such an examination and was therefore the first to describe the spermatozoa. This name was given to the motile element in the semen by von Baer in 1827. At this stage it was still thought to be a parasite (see later) and the modern name still commemorates this view. During the period under discussion, these objects were referred to by a variety of names —'animalcule', 'spermatick worms', etc., and these were spelt in many different ways. For clarity and convenience I shall use 'spermatozoa' throughout. However, others made the discovery almost simultaneously and his observations soon received independent confirmation. He described his discoveries in a letter which was written to the Royal

Society in 1677 but which was not published until 1679. Like all Leeuwenhoek's writings, the letter was originally in Dutch but appeared in a Latin translation (English translation in *11*, p. 9). The reason it was not translated earlier was not because it was regarded as unimportant but because (as Cole suggests) it was thought improper to make any reference to the details of sexual matters in a vulgar tongue. This convention was carefully observed by the Royal Society throughout the seventeenth and eighteenth centuries; even when the article is written in English, the author usually uses Latin expressions which become semi-technical and semi-polite forms of diction. Some examples of this are apparent in later quotations. Leeuwenhoek recounted how a certain Mr Ham had visited him, bringing a tube containing human semen. According to Mr Ham, the specimen came from a man who had been with a woman suffering from gonorrhoea, and it contained living animals which were killed if the patient took turpentine. Leeuwenhoek, however, went on to state that he had himself seen thousands of such animalcules in the semen of healthy men. He reported that they were smaller than red blood corpuscles, shaped like an earth nut with a long tail, and that they moved in the more liquid parts of the material by lashing these tails. He mentioned that he had sometimes thought that he could see different parts within these bodies, but that he was not certain of this. Leeuwenhoek then reminded the Society that their secretary had, some three years before, requested him to examine various bodily secretions, and added that at first he had taken the animalcules for globules and that later he had (for reasons of prudery) been unwilling to continue or report on his investigations. He went on to discuss the structure of the thicker part of the semen, in which he claimed to have seen

> a great number of small vessels.
>
> And when I saw them, I felt convinced that in the full grown human body there are not any vessels which may not be found likewise in sound semen. (*11*, p. 12)

This last remark suggests that, at this time, Leeuwenhoek had at the back of his mind some theory of generation not unlike that of the early atomists, and that he regarded this thicker part of the semen as the more important portion. However, the Royal Society was primarily interested in the living creatures in the semen, so the secretary wrote back urging Leeuwenhoek to continue his work and to look for animalcules in the semen of all animals. By 1683 Leeuwenhoek was able to report that he had established their existence in many other species. Meanwhile, others were also reporting and describing these little animals in the semen. Huygens, who was actually the first to give a published account of Leeuwenhoek's discovery in the *Journal des Savants* (Paris, 1678), afterwards confirmed the facts for himself. Later in the same year a young man named Hartsoeker reported, through Huygens, the appearance of little eel-like animals in the semen of the cock.

These discoveries all created great interest and most learned societies discussed the spermatozoa, or even demonstrated them to their members. Apart from this, attention was further focussed on this work, for from 1694 onwards Hartsoeker made repeated attempts to claim that he had, in fact, made the original discovery.

In the fifty years following the publication of *De Generatione*, enormous advances had been made. Although the ovum in the modern sense had not been seen, the function of the ovaries in all vertebrates had been demonstrated. It was now recognised that the female contribution to generation was produced there, and that this contribution might either be retained in the uterus until the new organism was formed, or might be extruded to complete its development within a covering, as in the fowl. The equivalent physical origin of the semen in the testes had been known from antiquity, but now microscopic examination revealed the spermatozoa. It might be imagined that once all these facts were available, a fuller understanding of the nature of sexual reproduction would follow almost immediately. But this is not so, for the correct interpretation was to take almost two hundred years.

The spermatozoa in particular raised enormous problems which could not possibly be settled against the general background of biological knowledge in the seventeenth and eighteenth centuries. The most immediate puzzle was a matter of their structure. Leeuwenhoek ultimately claimed to be able to distinguish two kinds which differed in size, and he suggested that these might be the two sexes, the larger being the male and the smaller the female (*92*, g, abstract of letter, pp. 1120–34). But he never claimed to be able to make out any details of the parts within the spermatozoa. Indeed, he criticised severely the two authors who did make such claims. The first was Hartsoeker who, in 1694 in *Essai de Dioptrique* (published in Paris) depicted a little manikin sitting within the head of the sperm. This diagram is familiar to all students of the history of biology, for it has been very frequently reproduced and has led to the idea that this interpretation of the spermatozoa was generally held in the seventeenth century. In fairness to Hartsoeker, it should be noted that he only claimed that his homunculus was what would be seen if the skin of the spermatozoa could be removed. Moreover, he later abandoned the idea that there would be any such fully formed embryo within a spermatozoon, and finally abandoned the whole theory of preformation, because he felt that it was inconsistent with the facts of regeneration.

The author who actually went so far as to claim that he had seen spermatozoa slough off their skins and reveal complete miniature men within, was Dalenpatius. His letter was published in 1699, simultaneously in Amsterdam, London and Edinburgh (*14*). In spite of the fact that he described the spermatic crystals found in human semen, and had therefore probably made some actual observations, most contemporaries dismissed his alleged findings. Leeuwenhoek was probably correct when, in commenting on the letter, he predicted that

> he was certain the Royal Society would have none of the seminal homunculus.
> (*15*, and comment in *92*, e)

Indeed, it was soon suggested that the whole letter was the work of a man named Plantade, and that it was intended as a hoax.

But while the majority of the naturalists did not go as far as to claim that they could discern complicated structures within the spermatozoa, they were by no means clear as to what they did expect to be able to see. In part their expectations depended on their view of the function and nature of these animalcules. There were three possibilities which were all seriously entertained. The first view was that the spermatozoa were not part of the semen itself, but were extremely ubiquitous and selective parasites. The second view was that they were the essential part of the semen, containing the embryo to be, and that they represented the male contribution in generation. The third view accepted the spermatozoa as a genuine part of the semen, but denied them any direct role in fertilisation, and usually denied that they were in any sense autonomous living units.

The idea that the spermatozoa were parasites was a fairly natural one. The microscope had revealed little animals in various secretions and organs, as well as in pond water and in concoctions of hay, grain and meat. Leeuwenhoek himself had observed living organisms in the tartar from his own teeth and 'worms' had been found fairly frequently in the intestines, ovaries and blood of numerous animals. The number and appearance of the spermatozoa perhaps favoured the view that they were parasites. But one might have expected it to have been dismissed as more and more reports came in of the presence of the spermatozoa in the semen of mature animals, and of their absence from the semen of very old or very young males.

However, microscopes were still poor and techniques very imperfect, so that not all investigators could find spermatozoa. For example, Maître-Jan (*50*) admitted that, although he had searched in the semen of dogs, cats, cocks and bulls, he himself had never observed them. He did not deny their existence, not their importance, and attributed his failure to the defects of his microscope. Others were less modest, so that there was, throughout the eighteenth century, still an element of doubt about the incidence and universality of these animalcules.

At first some had suggested that they might arise in decaying semen as the result of putrescence. But, in 1679, Hooke and others demonstrated that the little animals were present in juices obtained from the actual testes of a horse. He later reported that he had failed to find them in a young lamb and a very young cock. Of course, Hooke's demonstration did not preclude the possibility that the spermatozoa were parasites in the testes themselves. Indeed, the parasite view lingered on, not only in the eighteenth century but even in the nineteenth. In 1840, Gerber (*32*) and others were still discussing where they should be placed in a classification of the lower animals, and as late as 1835 Owen (*60*, pp. 387–94) classified them as parasites belonging to the order Prothelmintha, within the Entozoa. The modern name, 'spermatozoa', introduced by von Baer, 1827, commemorates this parasite view.

However, the vital appearance of the spermatozoa and their presence in the testes of the mature male did convince many that they were not parasites but the essential part of the semen. At this time the majority of the biologists accepted preformation which, of course, entailed that only one sex could donate the true embryo, but now there was an alternative to the 'ovum' as the source of the preformed germ. Moreover, those who believed that the preformed germ was the spermatozoon—the animalculists—had the advantage over the ovists in that their view restored the male to the more important position in reproduction, and was thus in line with all tradition. In addition, they could point to a visibly moving, and therefore living, object as their postulated germ. This version of preformation, which was suggested by Leeuwenhoek in 1683 (*92*, b, pp. 347–55), soon became fairly popular, although it never won universal assent, and some prominent naturalists, including John Ray (*64*), continued to oppose it. One difficulty was that since only one spermatozoon could be involved in each conception, animalculists had to admit to an enormous wastage of spermatozoa. On this point the theory was correct, and Leeuwenhoek justified it by pointing to an equal wastage of seeds; but as long as the spermatozoa were regarded as preformed animals this answer seemed inadequate. In the case of man himself the theologians were opposed because, they argued, if the spermatozoa played the role assigned to them in this theory, each one of them must have a rational soul, and God would never permit such wastage.

In spite of this objection, the animalculist version of preformation gained adherents, not only amongst the naturalists but also amongst a wider public, including many medical men, amongst them Andry, Geoffroy, Du Cerf and even Boerhaave. Throughout the eighteenth century semi-popular expositions of the theory continued to appear in both England and France. The last and most famous of these to appear in Britain was *The New Theory of Generation* by J. C. (Dr J. Cooke), which was not published until 1764—by which time the theory was certainly not new and had indeed been abandoned by most of the scientific élite. It is not really surprising that animalculism had this wide appeal for in many ways it certainly gave, within the limitations imposed by the general biological position, the clearest and simplest account of the known facts.

Leeuwenhoek's own exposition of his theory appeared in a series of letters which were published intermittently in the *Transactions* of the Royal Society (*92* (b) pp. 74 and 347; (c) p. 1120; (e) pp. 270 and 301; (f) p. 379; (h) p. 151). Although he discussed many points in great detail, the account is, of necessity, rather unsystematic. Many other animalculists such as Andry (*1*) and Bradley (*9*) referred to certain aspects of the theory or defended certain points but did not give a complete account. One of the earliest and most systematic surveys of the animalculist position was given by Bishop Garden in a short essay 'On the

Modern Theory of Generation' (*29*). Garden started his work with a brief resumé of the latest discoveries concerning generation, which is interesting as it shows the attitude of a near contemporary to the events described in this work:

> You know how wide and unsatisfying men's conjectures were upon this head until this Age in which first the deservedly famous Dr Harvey discovered the proper place of the formation of the chick in the cicatricula of the egg and the formation of the parts as far as was discernible by the naked eye and after him Malpighius, by the help of exact glasses, observed the first rudiments of it there both before and after incubation: And R. de Graaf and others having upon many observations concluded that the 'testes foeminei' were the ovaries of the females and consequently that all animals were 'ex ovo', they began from here to infer that the rudiments of each animal were originally in the respective females and that the males contributed only to give a new ferment to the mass of blood and spirits, by which means a spirituous liquor (which the blood in its ordinary ferment could not produce) did insinuate itself into the sense ducts and pores of the rudiments of these animals which were in greatest forwardness in the ovary and so extend and enlarge all their parts and at last bring them to perfection as Mr Perrault does ingeniously discourse in the third part of his 'Essais de Physicque': Till now at least Leeuwenhoekh as discovered an infinite number of 'animalcula in semine marium' of all kinds which has made him condemn the former opinion about the propagation of all animals 'ex ovo'. Now upon comparing the observations and discoveries which have been made with one another; these three things seem to me very probable:
>
> 1 All animals are 'ex animalculo' [i.e. from preformed germs].
>
> 2 That these animalcules are originally 'in semine marium et non in foeminis'
>
> 3 That they can never come forward or be formed without 'ova in foeminis'.

Garden's first statement sounds a little ambiguous but, taken in context, it is clear that he is asserting his belief in preformation itself. He gives, in all, six reasons for this belief:

1 Malpighi's first view of the rudiment of the chick in the cicatricula showed it to be similar in shape to a spermatozoon—that is, of course, only a reason if one is already convinced of the importance of the spermatozoon itself.

2 When the chick embryo is examined with the naked eye, certain parts cannot be seen until the fifth day, but if a glass is used these same parts can be seen within 30 hours of the start of incubation. He concludes that such phenomena would be explained if one assumed that the parts were there from the start, but must be extended to a certain degree before they became visible with the aid of a glass, and still further before they can be seen with the naked eye. He then goes on to mention:

3 Swammerdam and the pupa.

4 Size is only relative.

5 The analogy between the seed and the embryo. All these, while they do not prove the case, 'joined they do mutually strengthen the hypothesis'. Finally

6 He points out that all attempts to account for the phenomena by appeal to the laws of motion, i.e. physical laws, have failed.

Having given his reasons for accepting the idea of preformation itself Garden then considers the evidence for what we should call the animalculist version. He points to the actual discovery, by Leeuwenhoek and others, of these moving objects in the semen of many animals, and to the resemblance in shape between Leeuwenhoek's animalcules and the earliest stage of the foetus as described by other workers. The assumption that the spermatozoa are the preformed embryos will, he thinks, best explain why the foetus only appears after fecundation and why 'wind eggs' will never produce chicks, and it will also explain why the cock can fertilise so many eggs by one treading.

Lastly, Garden points out that this theory will give complete meaning to the first prophecy of the Messiah—only Jesus is truly the seed of woman, all the rest of mankind is the seed of man.

Garden now considers the role of the female in sexual reproduction. First he points out that we know from studies on the hen's egg that the embryo can only develop at one place—in the cicatricula. He assumes that before a spermatozoon can develop it needs a special 'nidus' or nest to provide shelter and food, that the cicatricula provides such a nidus in birds, and that only those spermatozoa which are lucky enough to reach an unoccupied cicatricula can continue to grow.

Something similar must be necessary in viviparous animals, otherwise why should not all the spermatozoa start to develop at once? There is no evidence that this happens.

What then, he asks, is the equivalent of the cicatricula in these animals? It cannot be the wall of the uterus, for extra-uterine conceptions are known, and the developed embryo can be observed before it embeds in the uterine wall. Could it be, as de Graaf and others claim, and as could be proved if the ovaries of some animals could be removed, that the ovaries produce an egg—and, if so, could this egg be the requisite nidus? There are two objections to this idea. First, there is the distance between the end of the tubae or cornua uteri and the ovaries. But to this it may be replied that there is a like distance in the hen where there is no dispute. Moreover, de Graaf claimed that after coition the fringed edges of the tubae uteri come up closer to the ovaries, so that the actual space between the ovaries and oviducts is decreased. The second difficulty about the ovaries as the source of the 'ova' is that there is a difference in size between the Graafian follicles and the apertures of the tubes. But, says Garden, both de Graaf and Malpighi state that

> the bladders in the ovaries are not the ova, but serve to form the glandules within which the ova are formed, which break through a small papilla opening in the glandules which bears a proportion to the aperture of the tube.
> (*29*, p. 476)

Garden concludes that it is a product of these Graafian follicles which provides the first nidus for the animalcule, and which is the viviparous equivalent to the cicatricula. Hence, before development can take place a spermatozoon must penetrate into such an ovum. Where does this impregnation occur? Again Garden gets close to the truth, for he points out that not only are there extra-uterine conceptions, but that, although Harvey could find no mass of semen in the uterus, Leeuwenhoek has recently discovered 'animalcula seminis maris in cornubis uteri' (*92*, d, p. 1692). Hence he suggests that the ova are impregnated either in the ovaries or as they descend through the tubes towards the uterus.

This version of preformation gave, for the first time since Harvey's work became known, a physical account of conception itself which was in accord with both Harvey's and Leeuwenhoek's discoveries. The animalculist theory was reasonable and could account for the known facts, but it was difficult to get further confirmation for it. Nobody, so far as I know, did try to remove the ovaries from any animal but, had they been able to perform this operation, it would merely have served to confirm de Graaf's views on the origin of the viviparous ovum, which were not in dispute at this stage.

Actually, in 1691, Nuck (59) did a somewhat similar experiment—he opened up a bitch shortly after copulation had occurred and ligatured the horns of the uterus. After twelve days the animal was killed and foetuses were observed between the ligatures and the ovaries. Nuck concluded that this showed that the embryo must be derived from the ovaries alone but the animalculists replied that they, too, regarded the products of the ovaries as essential, and they argued that in this case either the spermatozoa had already reached a point beyond the base of the cornua before the ligatures were applied or, being so small, some had managed to pass through the ligatures themselves. This experiment therefore was not conclusive for either the ovists or the animalculists, nor was any more conclusive evidence forthcoming. In the general state of knowledge it was, perhaps, hardly possible not to accept some form of preformation: but within these limits animalculism certainly came very near to the physical truth about sexual fusion, which was not established until almost two hundred years later. But it must not be forgotten that it depended for its acceptance on one interpretation of the spermatozoa for which there was no direct evidence; other interpretations were equally plausible. No experiments were performed on the role of the spermatozoa in reproduction until the end of the eighteenth century, and by that time animalculism was in complete disrepute. Spallanzani (see account in Chapter 11), who performed these experiments, was himself an ovist but, as we shall see, the results of these experiments (which seem to us fairly conclusive) did not immediately reopen the question for any of his contemporaries.

The spermatozoa were regarded as independent living organisms both by the animalculists and by those who believed them to be parasites. Both these groups assumed, in accordance with their biological outlook, that each spermatozoon must contain a full complement of organs, though both denied that the organs could be seen. But there were always some who denied the independence of the spermatozoa, and claimed that they were simply part of the semen as the corpuscles are part of the blood. Such people often also denied their independent mobility, and suggested that they were being carried about by currents in the fluid. As early as 1698, Lister (*47*, p. 337 and reply *92*, e, p. 270) suggested that they were a part of the secretion in this sense, and that their function was to help in the act of ejaculation. Linnaeus subsequently claimed that they were really inert masses of fatty material. Maupertuis, Turberville, Needham and Buffon were amongst the increasingly large number who, towards the middle of the eighteenth century, offered alternative interpretations. In these cases, however, their views on the nature of the spermatozoa were closely connected with general ideas on generation which were very different from the preformation theory. These views will be considered in a later chapter.

5

New Discoveries and New Attitudes, 1680–1745

'The true system of the world has been recognised, developed and perfected. . . . In short from the earth to Saturn, from the history of the heavens to that of insects, natural philosophy has been revolutionised; and nearly all other fields of knowledge have assumed new forms . . .'
d'Alembert, ÉLÉMENTS DE PHILOSOPHIE, 1759

IN THE first half of the seventeenth century biology, as the general study of living things, had not really started, and the main fields of enquiry were still comparative anatomy and embryology, which had developed in connection with the medical schools. Investigations into these subjects provided the basis for the ovist version of preformation. But after about 1660 the use of the microscope became more common, and this led to the microscopic investigations of the semen and to animalculism. The other discoveries made by microscopists lent plausibility to the assumptions of preformation, but produced no results which had a direct bearing on generation. Towards the end of the seventeenth century the general position changed and the range of biological enquiry slowly but steadily increased. In particular, two quite different kinds of investigations produced results which had a marked effect on ideas on generations: these were the various studies on the lower animals and the studies connected with plants and their classification.

In 1668 Redi (*65*) demonstrated that the maggots in decaying meat do not arise spontaneously, but develop from eggs laid by adult flies. Meat protected from flies developed no maggots. This result was independently confirmed by Leeuwenhoek in 1687 (*93*). Swammerdam in 1669 (*79*, Part III, p. 80) proved that the insects found in various plant galls develop from eggs laid by certain flies, and this, too, was independently discovered, by Vallisneri (*83*, p. 181) and Malpighi. Thus, by the end of the seventeenth century, there was ample evidence against spontaneous generation within the insect group. There is, I think, little doubt that these remarkable investigations were undertaken at this particular time because the preformation theory was 'in the air'. Most of these investigators were, or became, preformationists, and a belief in preformation, as understood at this time, entails the rejection of spontaneous generation. Thus the attention of those interested in insects would naturally be directed to this question. If this is so, then this is one field where the preformation theory stimulated research of considerable importance—research whose results, in turn, gave additional support to this new theory of generation.

Henceforth anyone who wished, for theoretical reasons, to maintain that spontaneous generation occurred, had to concentrate on the parasitic worms or on the infusoria. At this time, opinion was against it even in the unproven cases. Leeuwenhoek maintained that the creatures he observed must, in spite of their numbers, come from 'seeds' in the air. Andry (*1*), the expert on the parasites, believed that these creatures too must come from similar parents, although, of course, he could not prove his belief.

Swammerdam (*79*, Part II) and Réaumur (*22*, Vol. I, pp. 343 ff.) solved the mysteries of metamorphosis and showed conclusively that the pupa is not an egg, but a stage of development in the life cycle of a single individual. Insects therefore conformed, in general, to the normal pattern of reproduction. Only one small group seemed to deviate, in several ways, from the general rule. This was the aphids, or plant lice, about whose reproduction there were a number of confusing and contradictory reports. Leeuwenhoek had noted that the young were present as miniature adults within the parent, and hence that the group was viviparous. There seemed to be no distinct males, so he suggested that aphids might be hermaphrodites. Other observers claimed that the group behaved like other insects: that there were two distinct sexes, and that the wingless female laid her eggs after copulating with a winged male. Réaumur confirmed Leeuwenhoek's report that the creatures were viviparous but, although he could find no males, he denied that the flies he examined were hermaphrodite. (*22*, Vol. III, p. 288 ff.) He suggested that either the young were produced without a male, or that copulation occurred before the birth. But he could prove neither hypothesis and eventually suggested that his young admirer, Charles Bonnet, should take over the investigation.

In 1740 Bonnet started his enquiries (*8*, a, p. 19) using the aphids found on spindle trees. Having imprisoned a newly born female he reared her in seclusion. Eventually she produced ninety-five young. Later he was able to rear ten generations of such lice without there being any males. Bonnet proved conclusively that these animals can reproduce parthenogenetically. He had not discussed his views on generation at this stage, nor did he point out the relevance of this discovery for the ovist version of preformation. But there can be no doubt that this discovery must have inclined him to the view, of which he later became the champion.

At the same time as Bonnet was investigating the plant lice, his relation, Trembley, was starting his investigations into the behaviour of the Hydra and its allies—a piece of research which had unexpected repercussions on the whole intellectual life of the eighteenth century. Leeuwenhoek had described these creatures, and noted that they could reproduce by buds which appeared on their sides. Trembley rediscovered both the single specimens and those which formed branched colonies, like little trees. At first sight the objects appeared plant-like—they were sessile and sometimes green. But examination showed that they possessed 'stomachs', caught food in their tentacles, were sensitive and could move. To Trembley's amazement, if they were cut, either horizontally or vertically, the parts could regenerate into completely new individuals. Trembley's discoveries were immediately communicated to the French Academy (*80*, pp. 33–4) and to the Royal Society (*81*, p. 169). By 1744, Trembley had produced a complete monograph (*82*) on the subject which had a very wide circulation. As a result, there was no naturalist of the period who did not refer to Trembley's 'happy discovery', and within the next few years Réaumur and Bonnet started investigations which showed the existence of the same regenerative powers in other animals, including a number of fresh-water worms.

There were several reasons why Trembley's discovery should have caused so much excitement. Firstly, there was, at this time, a revival of interest in the Greek idea of a Chain of Being. According to this view, all living things can be arranged in a continuous chain or ladder, starting with the simplest plants and continuing through the animals to man himself. This idea of a continuous series of living things played a very important role in the thinking of eighteenth century biologists. It provided a framework for their ideas on nature, it was the basis of their classificatory systems, it led to the first conceptions of evolution and it strengthened their belief in the 'oneness' of nature. When the idea first reappeared there seemed little difficulty in finding a hierarchy of organisation amongst the plants and also amongst the animals, but the transition from the plants to the animals was more puzzling. Trembley's polyp provided the perfect missing link, and hence seemed to confirm the whole system.

The second reason why Trembley's polyp seemed so important was connected with the problems of generation. Here was an animal which had the power to convert food and water into a replica of itself, no matter where it was cut. In other words it seemed to indicate the presence, in living matter, of a power of reproduction and organisation which was independent of the sexual act. As we shall see, Trembley's investigations were made at a time when, for theoretical and philosophical reasons, there was a great need for a non-preformationist view. Hence his discoveries were used to support a number of new theories of generation which dispensed with preformation (see Chapters 6 and 7), and they also caused drastic alterations within the preformation theory itself.

The second group of investigations to yield results of importance to the understanding of generation were those concerned with the generation and classification of flowering plants. The floral parts were traditionally thought to be merely a protection for the young seed, whose origin was unknown, and it had been assumed that they did not reproduce sexually. Towards the end of the seventeenth century the suggestion was made, independently in England and on the Continent, that plants might reproduce sexually. In 1682 N. Grew (*35*) compared the flower to an hermaphrodite animal, and suggested that the stamens corresponded to the male organs and the gynaecium to the female. In 1694 Camerarius of Tübingen (*10*) described how he had isolated a number of the seed-producing flowers of dioecious species, such as hemp, dog's mercury and spinach, from the pollen of their type, with the result that no seed was produced. He therefore claimed that the seed was produced as the result of a sexual process quite analogous to that in animals.

The discovery of plant sexuality itself simply stressed the importance of the sexual process but did not clarify any problems. The origin of the seed was no easier to understand than the origin of the foetus and both an ovist and an animalculist interpretation was applied to the facts. However, the discovery did open up some new enquiries. Camerarius himself suggested that it might be possible to produce new types of plant by crossing the female part of the flowers with pollen of another species. In 1718 Bradley (*9*, a) observed insects pollinating some tulips, and went on to suggest that several varieties of Auriculas which had appeared in English gardens were the result of accidental cross-pollination by insects of the original yellow and black types. It is interesting to note, in view of subsequent developments, that the idea that new kinds might be the result of cross-pollination was already in the mind of this gardener before 1720.

The seventeenth century workers accepted the idea that God had created each species, and their classifications were attempts to recognise, describe and arrange these natural groups. Variations were minor imperfections which must be ignored—major differences and deviations were all classed as monsters. But experience showed that there was less difference between the kinds than this view would suggest, that variations were more common, and that new types seemed to appear suddenly amongst the progeny of existing kinds. In 1719 Marchant reported the appearance in his garden of two new Mercurialis species which continued to breed true, and he suggested that occasionally new types might be produced which, once established, became new species (*52*, p. 59). In 1742 Linnaeus was brought a 'Peloric' variety of the common toadflax (Linaria vulgaris) which also bred according to type (*69*). Linnaeus recognised this as a new species, and gradually abandoned his belief that all the present species were created in the beginning. By 1760 he was prepared to suggest that God had created a few species in each group, but that interbreeding amongst these had produced many of the species we now recognise (*46*).

The occurrence of deviations, the intermediate appearance of hybrids and the appearance of new types all created great difficulties for the supporters of the preformation theory. Where, according to this theory, could major variations come from? Before 1744, when, as we shall see in the next chapter, Maupertuis attacked the whole theory from this point of view, the preformationists proposed various solutions:

(a) Some held that variations were always due to accidents which befell the developing germs; either two germs fused together to produce a monster with supernumerary parts (monster *par excés*) or part of the germ failed to develop (monster *par défaut*). On this view all abnormalities must consist of a superabundance or a deficiency of the parts.

(b) Others, concentrating on hybrids, such as the mule, suggested that the young germ, being very delicate, was susceptible to alteration, and that the form was altered by the food. Since, in both the ovist and the animalculist views, the first food was provided by that parent which did *not* produce the germ, the intermediate character of the offspring was thought to result from its early nutrition.

(c) Some were prepared to credit some of the many folk myths, and relied on maternal impressions and the like.

(d) Bolder theorists cut short the whole search for explanation, and simply asserted that some germs were originally created in a different form. A dispute between Lemery, who held that monsters were the result of various accidents, and Winslow, who thought some germs must have been created as deviants, continued in the Académie des Sciences in Paris from 1724 to 1740 (*45*, and see Maupertuis *19*, a, pp. 78–83).

On the whole, then, the new discoveries made during the first forty years of the eighteenth century produced a great many new difficulties for the preformation theory. The discovery that maggots and plant galls were not spontaneously generated and the discovery of parthenogenesis in the aphids seemed in accord with the theory; but the discovery of animal regeneration, the recognition of the intermediate character of hybrids, and the realisation that variation was common and that novelty could appear, all told against it.

While the range of biological studies was gradually increasing, profound changes were taking place in other fields. As a result of these changes new requirements were imposed upon all branches of learning. Descartes had insisted that all phenomena (except for some of man's activities) must be explicable in terms of matter and motion. Living things were, for Descartes, simply machines. At the end of his work on 'Man' he made the following famous statement of his view:

> . . . I desire you to notice that these functions [i.e. digestion, nutrition, beating of the heart, movement etc.] follow quite naturally in the machine from the arrangement of its organs, exactly as those of a clock or other automaton, from that of the weights and wheels, so that we must not conceive or explain them by any other vegetative or sensitive soul, or principle of motion and life than its blood and its spirits agitated by the heat of the fire which burns continually in its heart and which is of no other kind than all the fires which are contained in inanimate bodies.
> (*24*, a, p. 202)

But Descartes' overall assumptions did not merely entail that organisms should be regarded as machines, they also entailed that these machines should be produced by physio-chemical processes from inanimate matter. In 1648, two years before his death, Descartes attempted to give an account of the formation of the foetus according to his principles, but this was not published until 1662 (*24*, b). Thus Descartes' ideas on embryology had the misfortune to appear just as Harvey's work was becoming known, and at a time when all naturalists were stressing the importance of careful empirical enquiry. To such men, Descartes' work must have seemed retrograde and speculative. It was universally regarded with disfavour, and the immediate effect of its belated publication was not to promote his thesis that a physio-chemical account of the formation of an organism was possible, but rather to provide an argument against it. Thus Garden (*29*, p. 474) gave this as one of his reasons for accepting preformation, and commented:

> We see how wretchedly Descartes came off when he began to apply the laws of motion to the forming of an animal.

Even as late as 1749, Réaumur could still remember this and say

> The great Descartes did not presume so much upon the strength of his genius, when he tried to explain the formation of the universe, as he did when he attempted to explain the formation of man; nor was he, perhaps, himself over and above satisfied with his essay on the last subject, which was not printed until after his death.
> (*23*)

Despite his failure to produce a convincing account of the formation of a living thing, Descartes did have a great effect on the development of ideas on generation. If the seventeenth century could not accept his corpuscular theory, they were convinced by his idea that living things must be machines and, in so far as this view played a part in the acceptance of the preformation theory, Descartes is indirectly responsible for more of the subsequent development than appears on the surface. He had, moreover, introduced into European thought the idea that a physio-chemical explanation of generation might be possible, and, but for his influence, attempts to achieve this might not have been so frequent during the next three centuries. The present successes in this field owe something to Descartes' heroic attempt.

When Descartes was writing, there were only philosophical reasons for preferring the mechanistic type of explanation, but by the end of the seventeenth century the idea had received scientific vindication at the hands of Newton. Along with the triumph of mechanism had gone a greatly increased belief in the atomistic or corpuscular nature of matter. In the *Principia*, Newton had suggested that natural phenomena in general

> . . . may all depend upon certain forces by which the particles of bodies, by some causes hitherto unknown, are either mutually impelled towards one another and cohere in regular figures or are repelled and recede from one another.
> (57)

In the Opticks, Newton was obviously even more clearly committed to a corpuscular theory of matter, and many other prominent thinkers of the period, such as Boyle and Locke, gave their support to various versions of the same idea. Thus by the mid-eighteenth century, corpuscular theories in general had come to seem more plausible and more commonplace. Most of the scientists who were interested in the physical sciences would have inclined to some theory of this type. Yet these theories implied that *all* phenomena were to be explained in terms of the particles of matter, and this obviously included living things. Hence the attention of those who wished for a unified science of nature was again directed towards generation—a field in which, as we have seen, recent discoveries had produced difficulties for the preformationists.

6

Maupertuis' Views on Generation

'The Astronomers were the first to feel the need of a new Principle to account for the movement of heavenly bodies, and they thought they had discovered it in those movements themselves. Chemistry has since recognised the necessity, and the most famous chemists today admit Attraction and extend it further than the astronomers have done.

'Why, if this force exists in Nature, should it not have a part in the formation of animal bodies?'

Maupertuis, VÉNUS PHYSIQUE, 1745

ADVANCES in biology had given new grounds for thinking that both parents must contribute equally to the new organism, and physical and chemical discoveries had made it much more plausible to suppose that all phenomena must be explicable in terms of matter and motion. The time was ripe for the rebirth of the particle theories of generation. The first theory of this type to appear in the eighteenth century was that proposed by Maupertuis in 1744. Maupertuis was primarily a physicist and was to a large extent responsible for the introduction of Newton's works in France. In this respect he was typical of the sort of person to whom such theories appealed, but it cannot be said in this case that his interest in the subject of generation was either superficial or incidental. His remarkable biological writings have recently received more attention, largely due to the work of the American scientist, Professor Bentley Glass (see the articles by this author in *The Forerunners of Darwin*, 33).

He was forty-six years old, and already famous as a physical scientist, before he turned his attention to generation. His only biological works prior to this had been two brief essays *On Salamanders* and *On Scorpions*, which he sent, in 1727 and 1731, to the Paris Academy of Science. In both works he showed an interest in the reproduction of the animals, but did not discuss the theoretical aspects of generation. He was extremely fond of animals and liked, whenever possible, to surround himself with what amounted to a private zoo. It seems probable that the great insight shown in his later works on generation owed much to his long sustained interest in and observation of his pets, for there is ample internal evidence to show that he must have studied the matter long and intensively before he actually published anything on the subject. What appears to have stimulated his first serious essay on generation was the arrival in Paris, just before 1744, of a human 'monstrosity'—a young albino male Negro, aged about four or five, who was reported to be the child of normal Negro parents. This unfortunate child intrigued Paris society and provoked curiosity about the cause of the phenomenon. In 1744 Maupertuis published anonymously an essay entitled *Une Dissertation Physique à l'Occasion du Nègre Blanc* and followed it the next year with a small volume entitled *Vénus Physique* (*19*, a). This latter contained the original essay and a second part called *Une Dissertation sur L'Origine des Noirs*. (See also Cole, *11*, pp. 174–5.) The case of the albino Negro is not really discussed until the second essay. The contradiction between the content and title in the 1744 essay is in part explained by the author's preface to the 1745 edition, in which he states that in the original essay he had promised to account for the albino Negro but had not in fact done so, and was therefore bringing out a second volume.

The work, though obviously written for the general reader, nevertheless made important contributions to the scientific study of generation, and also to the new problem of the origin of species, which was beginning to attract a little attention. The first essay was mainly devoted to an historical review of the ideas of Aristotle, Galen, Harvey and Descartes on generation, and to a summary of the animalculist and ovist versions of preformation. Against both the latter, Maupertuis raised a number of minor objections, most of which were not new, having already been used by the preformationists themselves in the course of the ovist-animalculist controversy. Against preformation in general Maupertuis raised a much more serious and novel objection; he claimed that the facts of inheritance showed that both parents must contribute equally to the offspring (*19*, a, Ch. XIII, pp. 74–7).

Many people had referred to particular cases of inheritance in support of their ideas on generation, but relatively few attempts had been made to frame any general rules. Maupertuis not only tried to generalise, but he also argued from these generalised facts to a conclusion about reproduction itself. Thus his approach was extremely like our own. In the first essay he drew attention to the fact that the offspring usually shares certain characteristics with both the mother and the father, and that such characteristics reappear too frequently in different generations for them to be due to chance, so that some at least must be inherited. The same set of characteristics does not appear in all the offspring of the same parents, and a child will often inherit some of his father's characteristics, some of its mother's, and will have yet other characteristics intermediate in kind between those of his two parents. The child of a black father and a white mother, for instance, is usually olive-skinned, but in various other respects may resemble closely either the father or the mother. When different species are crossed, as in the case of the donkey and the mare, the offspring is a distinct animal—in this case the mule—and the alteration is so great that the animal is almost always sterile. Maupertuis suggested that if either version of preformation were correct the offspring ought to bear a more marked resemblance to one parent. How can the ovist account for the recurrence of the paternal characteristics, or the animalculist explain the reappearance of maternal features?

As we have seen, some ovists had already suggested that the ultimate form of the new organism could be greatly influenced by its early food and by the seminal fluid, which acted as the growth stimulant. The animalculists had also suggested that the ovum, which in their view merely provided the nourishment, had a similar effect. Leeuwenhoek had even suggested that new hybrids might be obtained by transplanting young seeds and animalculi of one species into another kind of mother (*92*, b, Letter 38, pp. 347–55). Maupertuis hinted at these explanations, but dismissed them in the following way:

> Can one imagine that the spermatic worm, because it has been nourished by the mother, will come to have her characteristics? Wouldn't it be more ridiculous to believe this, than to believe that animals have to resemble the foods that nourish them or the places they inhabit?
> (*19*, a, Chap. 13, p. 77)

Maupertuis then considered monsters, and showed that the various solutions suggested by preformationists were all implausible. His chief objection to this theory was that it could deal satisfactorily with neither the facts of inheritance nor with the occurrence of monsters. A secondary objection was that it was at variance with the facts of embryo development, as described by Harvey.

Maupertuis was prepared to assert that both parents must contribute to the offspring, but he only advanced his own ideas on foetal development as a tentative conjecture. He emphasised that his ideas on the subject were similar to those of Descartes. This was probably an appeal to the orthodox French regard for Descartes, but the two theories did indeed have much in common. Both assumed that each parent contributed a particulate secretion and that the new individual was formed from a mixture of the two. Both believed that the foetus was formed gradually, as the result of physical and chemical actions essentially similar to those in inanimate matter. Physics and chemistry had greatly advanced in the intervening century, so Maupertuis had more facts to draw on and his actual account was, therefore, both more plausible and more detailed than that of Descartes.

He began his account by drawing attention to the fact that

> when one mixes silver and spirits of nitre with mercury and water, the particles of these substances come together themselves to form a vegetation so like a tree that it is impossible to refuse it the name.
> (*19*, a, Chap. 17, p. 100)

This structure was known as the 'Arbor Dianae', and its appearance fascinated the eighteenth century chemists. Although they could not explain its formation they recognised that it was the result of chemical action. It provided a much more persuasive model for the chemical formation of a foetus than did the vague references to fermentation and brewing which Descartes and earlier writers had used. Maupertuis, influenced by Newton, regarded gravitational attraction as a fundamental physical force. But in this discussion he also referred to the work of Geoffroy (*31*, p. 102), who had devised a table of affinities between different chemicals, and who believed that chemical combination was brought about by an attractive force between the particles of the substances. If chemical action could achieve a complete structure like the 'Tree of Diana', why should it not also be responsible for the formation of a foetus? If attractive forces cause physical and chemical actions, might they not also explain foetal formation?

At this stage Maupertuis merely assumed that the two secretions both contained particles destined to form the different organs, and that the foetus developed gradually, as like particles were attracted to each other and combined. In later editions of *Vénus Physique* and in *La Système de la Nature*, he suggested that these seminal particles might come from the adult organs themselves. He even suggested that this might be investigated experimentally, and actually described the exact form of the experiments which were carried out, some hundred and fifty years later, by Weismann:

> As to the manner whereby, in the semen of each animal, particles like that animal are formed, it would be a bold conjecture, but one perhaps not destitute of all truth, to think that each part furnishes its own germs. Experiment could perhaps clear up this point, if one tried over a long period to mutilate certain animals generation after generation; perhaps one would see the parts cut off diminish little by little; perhaps in the end one would see them disappear.
> (*19*, b, Chap. 5, and *33*, p. 68)

Maupertuis suggested that, normally, particles from one of the parents united, according to their affinities, with corresponding particles from the other parent, so that each organ of the offspring would contain particles from both parents. Thus, as Bentley Glass has pointed out, the theory is almost logically equivalent to the Mendelian theory (*33*, p. 68). Maupertuis did not believe, however, that each of the seminal fluids contained precisely one set of particles, nor that it necessarily contained exact multiple sets. If sufficient particles were present the mother would give birth to more than one offspring. Monsters *par excès*—those with supernumary parts—would be formed if there were an excess of certain particles with sufficient power to unite with the normal combinations. The attractive force itself would ensure that these particles aggregated in the appropriate regions—that the surplus finger appeared on the hand and supernumary toe on the foot, and so on. If some particles were deficient in number or had too weak an attractive force, a monster *par défaut*—one with a deficiency—would result (*19*, a, Chap. 17, pp. 106–7).

This theory could explain the general facts of inheritance and the occurrence of monsters. Maupertuis showed that it could also explain hybrids and their sterility. He knew that a hybrid or 'mule' could not always be produced, especially if the two distinct species differed much in form. He suggested that hybridisation could only occur if the particles in the two different semina were sufficiently alike to combine with each other. If this were the case, each individual organ would be formed from an aggregate of slightly dissimilar particles. From this it would follow that the actual parts might be intermediate in character or assume the form of one or other of the parents (this would depend on the relative strength of the affinities concerned). But the overall impression would be of a new plant or animal of a roughly intermediate character. In a later work Maupertuis wrote as follows:

> Could one not say that in the parts of the hinny and of the mule, the elements having taken a particular arrangement which was neither that which they had in the ass, nor that which they had had in the mare; when these elements pass into the semens of the hinny and of the mule, the habitude of this last arrangement being most recent, and the habitude of the arrangement which they had had in the ancestors being stronger, because contracted over a greater number of generations, the elements remain in a certain equilibrium, and unite neither in one manner or the other?
> (*20*, and *33*, p. 70)

In the second part of *Vénus Physique*, entitled 'Une Dissertation sur l'Origine des Noirs', Maupertuis returned, when discussing the origin of different human varieties, to the problem of the white Negro. He started by describing the chief races of man and their geographical distribution. He pointed out that the preformationists must simply assume that the original parent contained the germs of all these races, an explanation which Maupertuis dismissed as too facile. He pointed out that individuals having new characteristics do occasionally appear. Some new types, like the white Negro, are so obvious that they cannot be overlooked; others are less remarkable. Maupertuis knew that certain traits could remain hidden through several generations, only to reappear as the result of some fortuitous mating. Some apparently new kinds may have arisen in this way; if the white Negro were an example of this phenomenon, it need not have either a white mother or a white father.

> . . . it is enough that this child had some white Negro amongst its ancestors.
> (*19*, b, Chap. 4, p. 148)

Such cases could be explained by Maupertuis' particulate theory of inheritance as follows:

> . . . elements which represent the condition of an ancestor rather than the immediate parent may enter into the union forming the embryo and so produce a resemblance to that ancestor rather than to the parent.
> (*19*, b, Chap. 5, p. 157)

But all variation must have a beginning, and Maupertuis was prepared to say that a white Negro child need have neither white parents nor a white ancestor.

> . . . perhaps it was the first white Negro of its race.
> (*19*, b, Chap. 11, p. 148)

Maupertuis believed that new forms must arise as the result of chance changes in the form or arrangement of the seminal particles; he believed, in fact, that the ultimate source of novelty was mutations.

> Again one sees the birth, and even amongst us, of other monsters which are the result of nothing but chance combinations of the parts in the seminal liquid, or the efforts of too strong or too weak affinities between these parts.
> (*19*, b, Chap. 7, p. 166)

Once the new trait appeared it might become a true variety by repeated generation or disappear as the result of interbreeding with normal individuals. On the whole, Maupertuis thought, such novelties tended to disappear unless something unusual intervened.

> What is certain is that all the varieties which can characterise new species of animals and plants tend to become extinguished: they are deviations of Nature, which she preserves only through art or system. Her work always tends to resume the upper hand.
> (*19*, b, Chap. 5, pp. 159–60)

If, by some chance, such spontaneous changes could be reinforced by the appropriate breeding, they might then become established varieties. If the white Negro were to discover a white Negress and have a child by her, the child might well be black, since the ancestors of both were black. But if this child mated with another white Negro, and this were repeated for several generations then, according to Maupertuis, a race of white Negroes might result. In fact, as he explained later, white Negro families do occur fairly frequently in Senegal and an albino race of American Indians had been reported from Panama (*19*, b, Chap. 4, p. 149).

In order to show that new kinds could be established by the means suggested, Maupertuis drew attention to the work of the breeders. In a passage which sounds as if it came straight from *The Origin of Species* he explained:

> Nature contains the basis of all these variations: but chance or art brings them out. It is thus that those whose industry is applied to satisfying the taste of the curious are, so to say, creators of new species. We see appearing races of dogs, pigeons, canaries, which did not all exist in Nature before. These were, to begin with, only fortuitous individuals: art and the repeated generations have made species of them. The famous Lyonnais every year created some new species, and destroyed that which was no longer in fashion. He corrected the forms and varied the colours: he has invented the species of the harlequin, the mopse, etc.
> (*19*, b, Chap. 3, pp. 140–1, and *33*, p. 75)

This deliberate selection need not be restricted to animals. The sultans, interested only in the physical charms of their women, could breed new types if they wished. In fact, a previous king of Prussia, who collected about him an army of giants, had incidentally increased the average stature of his people (*19*, b, Chap. 3, p. 143). Some selection does occur amongst humans, there is a distaste for deformities, so these traits have less chance to become fixed by generation: taste and standards of physical beauty, on the other hand, help to preserve the types we admire (*19*, b, Chap. 3, p. 142).

Given that variations do occur, and that such variations could give rise to distinct varieties if the possessors of the traits interbred amongst themselves, could the races of men have appeared in this way? Maupertuis suggested that such deviations would be regarded as monsters. Possessors of these traits would tend to be driven away from the centres of population, and would retreat to the torrid or frigid regions where, in isolation, they might well give rise to distinct kinds. Climate and food might also affect the issue. Maupertuis thought that these might act on the hereditary particles and predispose them to some changes. Perhaps this partly explained why only dark-skinned races are found in the tropics.

> I do not exclude the influence that climate and foods might have. It seems that the heat of the torrid zone is more likely to foment the particles which make the skin black.
> (*19*, b, Chap. 5, p. 158)

Maupertuis thought it possible that acquired characters might be inherited. He did not regard this as a certainty, as Lamarck did, but suggested that it was a matter which should be investigated experimentally:

> To find out if the artificial singularities of animals pass, after several generations, to animals born from them, would certainly be something well worth the attention of philosophers. If tails or ears, cut off generation after generation, do not diminish or completely vanish in the end . . .
> (*19*, b, Chap. 5, p. 159)

The *Vénus Physique* was written for the general reader so, apart from the details he had collected about white Negroes, Maupertuis described no experiments or observations he had made on the subject of inheritance. Professor B. Glass records that an account or reference to Maupertuis' work on polydactyly appears in *Vénus Physique*, though there is no overt reference to it in the first edition, it may, of course, appear in later versions. It is perfectly apparent that he had already done much work on the subject: no-one could have shown such insight without having studied many examples in detail. In his later works he recorded three of his investigations, the most famous of which is that into polydactyly. This was most fully described in *Lettres de M. de Maupertuis* (*21*), but was also referred to in *Système de la Nature* (*20*). The account in the *Lettres* is as follows:

> A great physician proposes in a useful and inquiring work (*L'art de faire éclore des oiseaux domestiques*, par M. de Réaumur, t.II, mem. 4) to perform some experiments on this question [of biparental inheritance]. In the race (genre) of fowls it is not rare to see types (races) which bear five toes on each foot: it is hardly more to see those which are born without rumps. M. de Réaumur proposes to mate a hen with five toes with a four-toed cock, a four-toed hen with a five-toed cock; to do the same experiment with the rumpless cocks and hens: and [he] regards these experiments as able to decide whether the foetus is the product solely of the father, solely of the mother, or of the one and the other together.
>
> I am surprised that that skilful naturalist, who has without doubt carried out these experiments, does not inform us of the result. But an experiment surer and more decisive has already been entirely completed. That peculiarity of the supernumerary digits is found in the human species, extends to entire breeds (races); and there one sees that it is equally transmitted by the fathers and by the mothers.

Jacob Ruhe, surgeon of Berlin, is one of these types. Born with six digits on each hand and each foot, he inherited this peculiarity from his mother Elisabeth Ruhen, who inherited it from her mother Elisabeth Horstmann, of Rostock. Elisabeth Ruhen transmitted it to four children of eight she had by Jean Christian Ruhe, who had nothing extraordinary about his feet or hands. Jacob Ruhe, one of these six-digited children, espoused, at Dantzig in 1733, Sophie Louise de Thungen who had no extraordinary trait: he had by her six children; two boys were six-digited. One of them, Jacob Ernest, had six digits on the left foot and five on the right: he had on the right hand a sixth finger, which was amputated; on the left he had in the place of the sixth digit only a stump.

One sees from this genealogy, which I have followed with exactitude, that polydactyly (six-digitisme) is transmitted equally by the father and by the mother: one sees that it is altered through the mating with five-digited persons. Through these repeated matings it must probably disappear (s'eteindre); and must be perpetuated through matings in which it is carried in common by both sexes.
(*21*, Vol. II, Letter XIV, and *33*, pp. 63–4)

(The genealogy is given in diagram p. 81).
Maupertuis traced this family tree through four generations and produced mathematical evidence to show, beyond all reasonable doubt, that the trait of polydactyly was inherited.

But if one wished to regard the continuation of polydactyly as an effect of pure chance, it would be necessary to see what the probability is that this accidental variation in a first parent would be repeated in his descendants. After a search which I have made in a city which has one hundred thousand inhabitants, I have found two men who had this singularity. Let us suppose, which is difficult, that three others have escaped me; and that in 20,000 men one can reckon on one six-digited: the probability that his son or daughter will not be born with polydactyly at all is 20,000 to 1; and that his son and his grandson will not be six-digited at all is 20,000 × 20,000 or 400,000,000 to 1: finally the probability that this singularity will not continue during three generations would be 8,000,000,000,000 to 1; a number so great that the certainty of the best demonstrated things of physics does not approach these probabilities.
(*21*, Letter XIV, and *33*, p. 72)

It is interesting that Maupertuis here foresaw that the preformationists would attempt to deny that the characteristic was inherited, and would wish to ascribe the occurrence to chance in each generation. It was his evidence *against* the chance explanation which compelled Charles Bonnet to abandon it.

Bentley Glass comments:

> This is not only an excellent example of scientific caution, but also represents what is without doubt the first application to genetics of one of the most important of the principles of the mathematics of probability, that of the probability of coincidence of independent items. It was this very principle that Mendel applied so effectively in his analysis of segregation, random recombination, and independent assortment.
> (*33*, p. 72)

Evidence of the inheritance of polydactyly was perhaps the most telling fact against preformation that was produced throughout the eighteenth century. The appearance of 'monsters' was difficult, isolated instances of inheritance from one generation to the next could be accommodated, but a genealogy showing that a certain characteristic could be handed on by either sex for many generations was a different matter.

Maupertuis' account of the inheritance of polydactyly was not the only one to appear at this time. In 1751, a year before the publication of the above account in Maupertuis' *Lettres*, Réaumur published a very similar pedigree of the Kelleia family (see diagram on p. 81). This information had been sent to Réaumur by M. de Reville, Commander of Malta, and appeared as an appendix to the second edition of *L'Art de Faire Éclore et d'Élever en Toute Saison des Oiseaux Domestiques de Toutes Espèces* (*23*, a). Neither Réaumur nor Maupertuis mention the pedigree supplied by the other. Was it then pure coincidence that both should produce, almost simultaneously, such similar evidence concerned with the same abnormality?

The facts appear to be as follows:

Maupertuis published *Vénus Physique* in 1745, and for the first time stressed the importance of the study of heredity.

Réaumur read *Vénus Physique* before 1749, for, in the first edition of *L'Art de Faire Éclore* in 1749, he gave an unmistakable account and criticism of Maupertuis' theory (see p. 83). He did not mention Maupertuis by name, presumably because *Vénus Physique* was published anonymously, but he did, in the same chapter, urge the study of inheritance and suggest that a five-toed variety of fowl might be crossed with the usual variety.

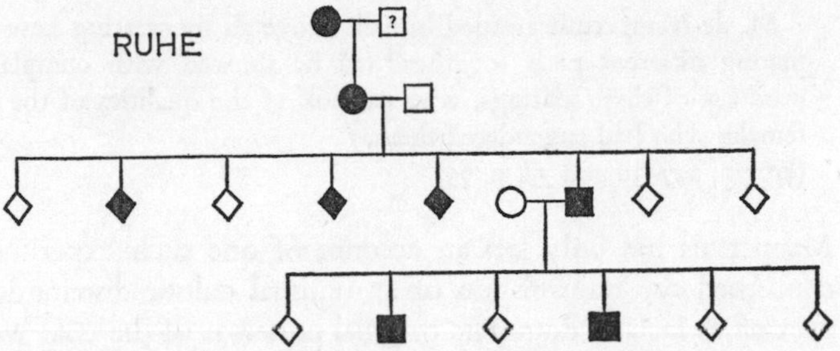

Polydactyly in the Ruhe family, according to Maupertuis

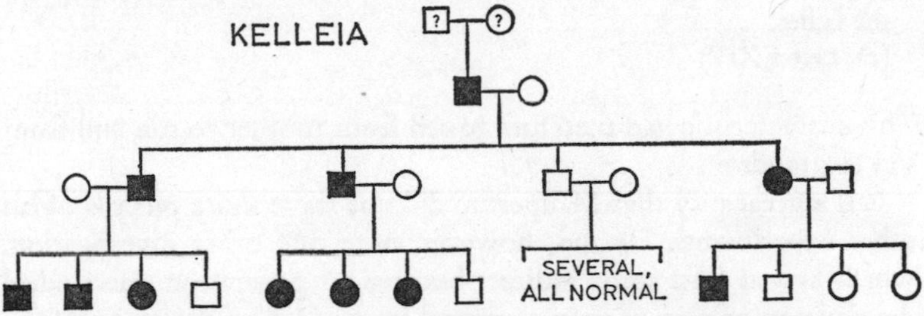

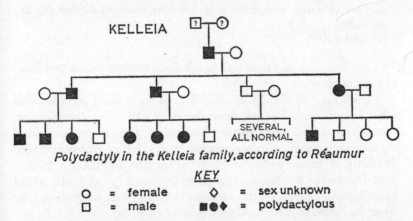

Polydactyly in the Kelleia family, according to Réaumur

KEY

○ = female   ◇ = sex unknown
□ = male   ■●◆ = polydactylous

From Forerunners of Darwin, *Ed. Bentley Glass, O. Tempkin and J. Strauss. Reproduced by courtesy of The Johns Hopkins Press.*

Maupertuis mentioned this work at the beginning of the quotation on p. 78 but had presumably read the first edition (1749) which did not contain the appendix.

It would seem probable that it was the mention of polydactyly in fowl which prompted M. de Reville to send Réaumur the account of the Maltese family. Maupertuis had certainly made an extensive study of heredity prior to reading Réaumur; but it may be that it was Réaumur's remarks which directed his attention to polydactyly.

As well as studying the Ruhe pedigree, Maupertuis conducted some breeding experiments. Samuel Formey, the secretary of the Berlin Academy, reported:

> M. de Maupertuis amused himself above all by creating new species by mating different races together, and he showed with complaisance the products of these matings, who partook of the qualities of the males and females who had engendered them.
> (*40*, pp. 217–30 and *33*, p. 73)

Maupertuis has only left an account of one such experiment. This concerned the transmission of an unusual colour distribution in the coat of an Iceland dog. The original possessor of the coat was a bitch who eventually produced, after three litters by different fathers, one male pup of a similar kind. The mother died, but from the dog,

> after sexual mating with different bitches there was born another dog like the father.
> (*21*, Letter XIV)

This characteristic had therefore passed from mother to son and from son to grandson.

It is a great pity that Maupertuis did not leave more records of his other experiments. He did, however, note one other investigation, which had at least some indirect bearing on generation. He studied the skeleton of a giant man preserved in the Hall of Anatomy of the Academy of Science in Berlin. He described how additional vertebrae were inserted in the lumbar region, and pointed out that this would be difficult to explain on the assumption that supernumary parts arise from the fusion of two preformed germs (*33*, p. 74).

Maupertuis achieved some remarkable insights. His penetrating analysis of the results of his investigations enabled him to see further than most of his contemporaries. If we think of his particles as being like genes in contemporary theory, the determinants of hereditary, then much of what he said has an amazingly modern sound. It is evidence of his genius that he could make so many correct inferences from the facts at his disposal. But Maupertuis was limited by the general state of biological knowledge. Before the cell theory was formulated, organs, as we have seen, were regarded as the basic units of any organism. Because of this well-founded belief, anyone who suggested that the foetus was formed from particles thought of these particles as making up the primordia of actual organs. Maupertuis, like all other eighteenth century thinkers, made this assumption, and therefore could not conceive of the particles all being enclosed within any object as tiny as a spermatozoon or an egg. He was thus forced to deny that the Graafian follicles produced anything like a female contribution to generation, or that there was an initial egg or primordium in Harvey's sense. He reverted to the old view that the ovaries were not directly concerned with reproduction, and that the vesicles seen there were the result of hydatid infection. According to Maupertuis the true female secretion was formed within the uterus. The whole of the semen, he thought, must be involved in the act of fertilisation. Although he did not deny the existence of the spermatozoa, he believed that it was solid particles in the semen which provided the essential elements. The spermatozoa were not independent organisms or parasites, but motile particles whose function was to agitate the commingled mass of the two semina, and thus facilitate the mixture of the essential parts.

Maupertuis obviously wished to provide a purely materialistic account of embryo formation. In his original version he suggested that a force, like gravity or chemical affinity, might act between the particles, and that this would cause the particles to come together—liver particles being attracted to liver particles, brain particles to brain particles, and so on. Such an attractive force, it was plausible to suppose, might well serve to collect the like material together, but most eighteenth century naturalists felt that it was inadequate to explain the formation of complicated organs and the production of a unified organism.

Réaumur criticised Maupertuis' ideas in the following way:

> Everything has its fashions nor is philosophy itself an exception to it: those occult qualities, those sympathies and antipathies which nobody would have dared to name in physicks fifty years ago, have, since that time, showed themselves again with splendour under the name of attraction: although we never were taught what this attraction consisted in, very noble uses have been made of it with regard to the motions of the celestial bodies; great efforts have been made likewise, to make it serve in general to explain all the phenomena in nature. People thought it might be usefully employed to disentangle all the materials which are to enter into the prolifick liquors; it was deemed capable of operating the miracle of the formation of the foetus; in order to which people judged it sufficient to suppose that the similar parts of one and the same kind had the property of mutually attract-

ing one another, and that there were different laws of attraction for similar parts of different kinds: by virtue of these laws, all the similar parts fit to make a heart, all those fit to make a stomach, a brain, etc. will seek for their own kind, draw near and unite with them: the chaos is now clearing apace, and innumerable masses composed of the most analogous parts are going to be formed. We are nevertheless as yet very far from seeing anything that resembles any of the organisations which are to concur towards the formation of our great work: how will attractions be able to give to such and such a mass the form and structure of the heart, to another that of the stomach, to a third one that of the eye, and to another that of the ear? How will they frame other masses into vessels, valves, etc. All their tendency will amount barely to the reunion of the similar parts into solid masses. What law of attraction shall one imagine for the making of that small bone of the ear, whose figure makes it to be called the stirrup? How shall so many different organs be placed and assembled in their proper order? We see with the most glaring evidence, that in order to arrive at the formation of so complicated a piece of work, it is not enough to have multiplied and varied the laws of attraction at pleasure, and that one must besides attribute the most compleat stock of knowledge to that attraction. (*23*, b, p. 462)

Maupertuis himself was troubled by the same kind of considerations and, in the *Système de la Nature*, he ceased to rely on the force of attraction alone. It was perhaps because he felt that matter endowed only with the power of attraction could not account for the organisation of living things that he became interested in the philosophy of Leibnitz. His final views were neither Newtonian nor Leibnitzian, but a unique blend of the two. Still convinced that all phenomena must be explicable in terms of the universal properties of matter, he suggested that all matter was endowed with a kind of 'memory' or 'organising power', which, in certain circumstances, caused it to reform into complicated patterns. When, in 1751, he returned to the subject of foetal formation he suggested:

> The elements suitable for forming the foetus swim in the semens of the father and mother animals, but each, extracted from the part like that which it is to form, retains a sort of recollection of its old situation, and will resume it whenever it can to form in the foetus the same part.
> (*20*, Section XXIII)

Maupertuis' works on generation were widely known, and were

commented on by a variety of contemporary authors including Réaumur, Buffon and later Haller and Bonnet amongst the biologists: and more generally amongst those who looked for a materialistic interpretation of nature, such as Diderot and Robinet. The pedigree of the Ruhe family was however usually ignored in these accounts. Although *Vénus Physique* was published anonymously and the *Système de la Nature* appeared under the pseudonym of Dr Baumann, their true authorship was an open secret. That a scientist of Maupertuis' standing should have proposed an alternative to the preformation theory was of great importance. Many thinkers, especially in France, were convinced that it should be possible to give a materialistic account of living things; the stumbling block was that, prior to this, most of the leading naturalists had agreed that the formation of organised beings could not be explained in this way. The very fact that one such theory had been proposed by a reputable investigator made it easier for them to develop versions of their own. Most of the materialists of this period wished to use their systems to support conclusions about the moral nature of man and about his social systems. They often disagreed with the later version of Maupertuis' theory because of the assumption that matter must possess some kind of memory. In any case they were not concerned with the detailed observations on which this system was based, and paid no attention to Maupertuis' important suggestion that the facts of inheritance should be investigated with more care.

7

Other Mid-Eighteenth Century Ideas on Generation: Buffon, Turberville Needham, Koelreuter and Linnaeus

'The intelligence which can reproduce the lost claw of a crayfish can reproduce the entire animal.'

Hartsoeker, 1722

MAUPERTUIS was aware of Trembley's discovery of the regenerative power of the polyps, but he based his case against preformation almost exclusively on the facts about hybrids, monsters and inherited variation. Subsequent developments have vindicated his approach, but to those eighteenth century naturalists who wished to refute preformation the facts of regeneration seemed a more promising line of attack. That this should be so, shows how deeply concerned most naturalists were about the problem of the organisation of living matter. The preformationists were forced back to their theory because they could not see how creatures, with the complicated organisation which living things possess, could possibly arise from unorganised matter: any attempt to produce a unified materialist view of nature was defeated at this point. There were other vital processes—nutrition, animal heat, respiration and the like—which could not be explained in physio-chemical terms. But these, at this stage, seemed less of a problem for the mechanist: it was the reproduction of the complicated vital organisation which presented the major difficulty. Trembley's discoveries solved nothing, but at least they showed that the generation of animals was not entirely restricted to the sexual process. They thus held out the hope that, by investigating the simpler cases, one might discover the genesis of organisation itself. This is one reason why Trembley's discoveries provoked so much interest, and why they stimulated Bonnet,

Réaumur and later Spallanzani to investigate this regenerative power in other animals. Within a few years new theories about the nature of living things appeared which, if they were not the direct result of the work on hydra, were certainly formulated with this in mind.

The best-known theory of this type was produced by de Buffon, and published in 1749 in the volume of the *Histoire Naturelle* entitled 'Des Animaux' (*16*). The theory, a variant of the Epicurean view which had been re-introduced into European thought by Gassendi, covered all vital phenomena and was not just confined to sexual reproduction. It was an ingenious attempt to explain regeneration and growth without either assuming *emboîtement* or suggesting that organised living things could arise from simple inorganic matter.

Buffon started by drawing attention to the fact that, whereas there is no sharp distinction between plants and animals, for there are transition forms such as Hydra, there is a sharp line between animate and inanimate. All animate matter clearly differs from inanimate in being able to grow and reproduce. Buffon accordingly assumed that the matter in the Universe was of *two* fundamentally distinct kinds, *organic* and *inorganic*. The former was made up of primary particles which were vital, identical and indestructible. These atoms had a tendency to unite to form groups with a definite pattern. Just as a grain of salt was made up of numerous smaller grains, so organisms were composed of numerous minute replicas of themselves (*16*, Chap. 2, p. 24)—each unit being a group of the primary particles. Growth could be explained by assuming that the vital organic particles, liberated from other bodies after death, entered the soil and air and were eventually taken in by plants. Within the plants the vital particles reformed into new groups like those already there, and so the plants grew. A certain amount of inorganic matter was always present within plants and animals, dependent either directly or indirectly on plants for food, always obtained a mixture of organic particles and inorganic material. The food was broken down into its constituents in the digestive system, and some of the inorganic matter was given off as excretions, but the essential organic particles were absorbed into the organism, where they reunited with the units already present to form more identical organised groups. Thus both plants and animals grew by the constant addition of more minute replicas of themselves, formed by the identical and basic organic particles. De Buffon described his theory as follows:

> For the reasons just given it seems to me highly probable that there really exist in Nature an infinity of little organised beings, similar in all respects to the larger organised beings to be found in the world—that these little organised beings are composed of living organic parts which are common to animals and vegetables—that these organic parts are themselves primitive and incorruptible parts—and that organised beings are visibly formed by the grouping of these parts, and that reproduction and generation are therefore nothing but a change of form which comes about simply by the addition of these similar parts, just as the destruction of living things comes about by the division of these same parts (into their primitive and incorruptible vital particles). (*16*, Chap. 2, p. 2)

How do the identical vital particles come to take up the patterns which form the basic units of each individual? Buffon believed that each organism possessed a force or property, which he called the 'interior mould' (*moule intérieur*). A mould imposes, from the outside, a certain shape upon the matter which fills it. By placing matter in a mould we may produce any number of identical forms. By analogy, Buffon suggested, there is within each organism a force or power which, like a mould, imposes upon the identical particles the form which is peculiar to that individual (*16*, Chap. 2, p. 35). Maupertuis had tried to explain generation by supposing that there were *unique particles* acted on by a *universal* force, but because no simple attraction seemed adequate, he later endowed this force with a memory which would be different in each different case. Buffon, from the first, made his force *unique in the different organisms*, but *universal* in *respect of the type of action it performed*. He could not, of course, give any account of how such forces might arise, nor could he describe in detail how they could act. It is clear, however, that he felt justified by the behaviour of living things in postulating the existence of these forces, and that he believed that in so doing he was employing the method used with such success in physics (*16*, Chap. 3, pp. 50 and 53).

Crude as this theory seems to us, it nevertheless contains some important insights. By considering the general facts of growth and regeneration in all living things Buffon had been led to make many correct inferences. He saw, for example, that there must be cycles in nature, that all living things destroy in order to obtain material for growth and reproduction and that:

> . . . after flame, animals are the greatest destroyers.
> (*16*, Chap. 2, p. 40)

Buffon knew nothing of the plants' power to synthesise sugars, but it seemed evident to him that the material must be returned as dead matter decays. Birth, growth, death and decay are, for him, a genuine cycle involving the vital particles. Similarly he realised that, if it were not assumed that all organisation is imposed upon living matter at creation, then living things must have within themselves the power to annex certain substances from food, and to incorporate them as part of their structure. From the facts of growth and regeneration Buffon rightly concluded that living things must be composed of structured units, and that these units must be able to produce more units like themselves. He was, of course, wrong in assuming that the organised parts were in any way replicas of the whole, and he seemed to forget that the groups of particles are supposed to be replicas especially when he discussed the higher animals and their reproduction, but he probably came as near to inferring the cell theory as was possible on the mere facts of regeneration.

Buffon's theory explained growth and the reproduction of the whole from a part, but the majority of the higher organisms reproduce sexually. To explain this type of reproduction Buffon assumed that some of the surplus organic particles, which had been received into all the various organs, were gradually liberated when such organisms reached maturity and that these surplus organised groups collected in the reproductive organs (*16*, Chap. 4, pp. 58–9). The seminal fluids, therefore, contained an assortment of organised units identical with those in the parent body. Buffon believed that the female contribution was formed in the Graafian follicles, but could not accept the idea of a single egg or primordium in Harvey's sense. The follicles must, he thought, produce a liquid like the semen, but not as prolific, which dripped into the uterus where, if coition had occurred, it intermingled with the semen. Similarly, the cicatricula in birds' eggs must also contain a mass of organic particles. The offspring was always formed from units donated by both parents, and its sex would be determined by whichever units happened to predominate (*16*, Chap. 4, p. 58). Buffon did not discuss inheritance in detail, but he did point out that his bi-parental theory was in accordance with the well-known fact that children resemble both parents; some children favouring one and some the other.

Buffon apparently formulated his theory some years before 1749, when he wrote *Des Animaux*. While in England (about 1738?) he met and discussed his theory with the Abbé Turberville Needham, a microscopist whom he persuaded to re-investigate the origin of the objects seen in infusions of plant and animal matter (*16*, Chap. 6, pp. 169–71 and *55*). It was generally assumed that these were genuine animals which arose from 'seeds' which had been present in the air. Buffon suggested, on the other hand, that the objects might merely be the products of decomposition and not living animals. According to his theory the almonds, and the various animal products within the infusion, were made up of dead organic matter which still contained the vital organic particles. Since the specific *moule intérieur* had been destroyed, the organised molecules of this matter could separate out, and would ultimately break up into their component particles. The Abbé Needham, having examined some infusions, inclined to Buffon's view. He believed that there were too many objects in the glass for each to have arisen from a seed, and their motion was not like that of independent animals (*54*). He reasoned that if they were living things they should not appear in infusions which had been tightly corked after being placed into phials while still at boiling point. The heat would kill anything in the liquid and the cork would prevent fresh access from the air. Needham was right, but unfortunately his corks were not tight, or else the covering was not sterile. Although he performed the experiment many times, the liquid always contained an enormous mass of the objects. Buffon concluded from this that his theory was correct, and that the moving objects were not independent living things but collections of vital particles (*16*, Chap. 6, pp. 170–3).

Buffon also believed that the spermatozoa found in the semen were simply a collection of vital particles, and tried to show that if the semen were left to decompose these spermatozoa would break up into the smaller particles. But it would follow, if he were correct, that the female secretion should also contain 'spermatozoa'. Aided by M. Dauberton and attended by M. Needham, Buffon proceeded to look for and find 'spermatozoa' in the Graafian follicles of a bitch who was on heat but had not been served, and he claimed that he had repeated this observation on numerous other female animals, and as far as I know, no-one has ever given a satisfactory explanation for this curious 'observation' (*16*, Chap. 6, pp. 201–21, Experiment 25–43). What was true of the spermatozoa and the infusoria could be extended to parasitic animals and to diseases of plants. Buffon now suggested that the 'worms' (i.e. parasites) in the stomach and intestines might arise from surplus molecules which had not been absorbed into the body, and that, in fact, all 'parasitic creatures' had a somewhat similar origin and nature. This appears in later editions of *Des Animaux* after 1802.

Buffon regarded embryo formation as a special case of growth and regeneration, and believed that it must proceed in the same manner. When the two secretions mixed, the vital molecules from both sexes must re-form to produce the initial groups of particles in the new individual. Buffon had claimed that, in plants and animals which can reproduce from any portion, the particles must all be replicas of the whole organism. When he came to consider the higher organisms he apparently believed this was not so, and that there were different groups of particles which represented the different organs (*16*, Chap. 11, pp. 366–7). Once the first groups representing the various parts had formed, the embryo grew as new groups of vital particles were intercalated between the original ones. In a sense, then, according to this theory, the embryo was formed or precipitated directly after the two semina mixed. Thus, though he dispensed with *emboîtement*, Buffon nevertheless retained a kind of preformation. He did not, of course, believe that the vital molecules could be seen, or that this preformation was in any way visible. When he spoke of the molecules being laid down in the two semina he was trying to explain embryo formation, not to describe it. This is made completely clear by his detailed and fairly accurate accounts of the development of the chick (*16*, Chap. 11, pp. 375–80) and the human embryo (*16*, Chap. 11, pp. 380–419), which followed the usual lines.

Whereas Maupertuis' ideas had interested naturalists, and shown that *emboîtement* could be questioned by a competent scientist, Buffon's ideas influenced a wider public. This was partly because the latter appeared in the *Histoire Naturelle*, the most comprehensive biological work yet produced. But it was also because his approach was more in tune with the times. Buffon attacked the problem of growth and regeneration, which was widely recognised and had been emphasised by Trembley's discoveries; whereas Maupertuis had concentrated on the inheritance of variations, a matter which was not considered important until after Darwin's work was understood. Thus the majority of the particulate theories which appeared after 1750 were variants of Buffon's views.

The Abbé Needham, whose researches on the infusions provided the 'factual' basis for Buffon's theory, produced his own views on generation (*56*). On the whole, Needham's theory was similar to Buffon's. He believed that the embryo was formed from sets of vital particles, provided by both parents. As he probably assisted Buffon with the observations on the ovaries of various animals, he naturally agreed with Buffon on this point. However there is no suggestion in Needham's writings that the organic particles form patterns which are replicas of the gross form of the organism, and Needham puts more emphasis on the existence of a vital force, which acted as the formative agent in all vital change. Needham believed that he had observed, in infusions, vegetables turning into animals and these in turn being converted into other vegetables.

These changes were due to the power of the vegetative force which was responsible for all vital manifestations including the gradual development of the embryo.

At first sight, Buffon and Needham seem to have almost identical views on vital organisation and it is difficult to see why they should be regarded as holding separate theories. However, there is an important difference between them which was probably more apparent to their contemporaries than it is to the twentieth century reader. Indeed on closer inspection it might almost be said that their ideas were in fundamental opposition. Buffon, throughout his work, emphasised the continuous variation which existed amongst living things. This was, in part, the natural outcome of the more detailed observations which had been made during the preceding century. It led Buffon to oppose the claim, made by Linnaeus, that the latter's system was a natural one. At the same time Buffon opposed the view that nature could be fully described in mathematical language. Both the emphasis on variation and the opposition to a mathematical science appealed to some of his immediate successors who were in revolt against all science and who used Buffon's writings to support their own views. Hence Buffon has sometimes been regarded as one of the first supporters of the romantic opposition to all science. The detailed studies of Professor Lovejoy (*49* and *33*) have convinced most historians that Buffon's ideas do differ very markedly from those of the Romantics. In a more recent article, Dr Wohl (*98*, pp. 186–99) has given what seems to be the correct analysis of Buffon's scientific methodology. He has pointed out that far from being opposed to Newton, Buffon believed that he was applying the same methods.

What makes Buffon a serious and significant figure in the history of science is that he grasped fully the significance of Newton's discoveries—not only for physics, but also their implications for scientific method. As a pioneer in natural history, Buffon understood the subtle line that Newton had drawn between an objective science that goes beyond the senses to comprehend hidden forces and a subjective science such as Lamarck's or Goethe's that would try to comprehend. His own scientific works . . . were attempts to apply this thought.
(*98*, p. 199)

Buffon was opposed to all attempts to impose upon nature a rationalistic or *a priori* scheme, but he was convinced that nature was lawful and that an objective science inferred from the observed facts was possible. His theory of vital activity was an attempt to arrive at such a theory. He believed that there was abundant empirical evidence for an impassable gap between inanimate matter and living things and it was on this basis that he thought himself justified in postulating the existence of two kinds of matter—inorganic and organic. Similarly the facts of growth, regeneration and reproduction led to the inference of the *moule intérieur*—just as the phenomena of free fall and planetary motion justified the assumption of universal gravitation. Newton could not give a causal account of gravitation nor could Buffon give any 'process account' of the methods by which his force might work. But Buffon was so impressed with Newtonian Physics that he was prepared to suggest that the *moule intérieur* was probably an attractive force.

Newton was able to supply a formula for the measurement and calculation of the force of gravity which greatly increased its explanatory and predictive power: naturally Buffon could do no such thing for the *moule intérieur*. It is little wonder that the latter was attacked as vague and useless nor that it was re-interpreted, by others, as if it were intended as a vehicle for subjective vitalism. There is, however, no evidence that Buffon himself, acting in accordance with his methodological principles, was prepared to make any assertion about the *moule intérieur* except for his speculation that this force might be of an attractive nature.

Buffon's writings contain a vast amount of description but, as Dr Wohl has noted, Buffon was intensely interested in scientific methodology and was attempting to put natural history into a new theoretical framework; his methodological comment can therefore be used as a clue to the exact meaning of his theoretical position. With Turberville Needham this is not possible: in spite of his many observational errors, Needham was essentially an experimentalist and his abilities in this field far exceeded those of Buffon. Needham's writings were mostly concerned with his observations and experiments, his theoretical comments were interwoven with his empirical results. It is therefore difficult to decide in what sense Needham intended his 'vegetative force' to be understood. Nevertheless his use of the concept suggests that he was prepared to assume that it had all and every feature necessary to *explain fully* all his observations, both correct and erroneous. His readiness to make assumptions about the method by which it operated hint that Needham had slipped, almost unconsciously, over the narrow line to which Dr Wohl referred when he spoke of the subtle distinction between an objective science and a subjective one. On this interpretation, Needham was really the first eighteenth century scientist to abandon all hope of a true science of vital organisation and to retreat into a form of subjective vitalism.

Retrospectively it is obvious that all eighteenth century workers were doomed to be defeated at this point—two centuries later we are still only moving slowly towards a complete understanding of the extremely complicated subject of vital organisation. However this defeat was not without its significance in the whole history of European thought: for it occurred just as the romantic, anti-scientific movement was already astir in Germany and it provided an insuperable obstacle for any honest thinker who wished to claim that the mechanistic sciences were capable of dealing with all the important aspects of nature.

The whole problem of generation was further confused during this period by the appearance of a new interest in that long neglected subject—botany. It now became fashionable for the learned to take an interest in gardens and in plants. The classificatory system invented by Linnaeus was relatively easy to understand and to use, so the naming and recognition of wild flowers and of imported specimens became a new pastime. Most of the leading botanists, including the master himself, were convinced that the higher plants reproduced sexually. The earlier writers on this subject, whose main aim was to establish the *fact* of plant sexuality, had attempted to explain the production of the embryo in terms of the current versions of the preformation theory. By 1760, however, the leading botanists were developing theories of their own which owed little to the prevailing views on animal generation.

Linnaeus himself believed that both sexes contributed material to the offspring, and that the female parent determined the form of the flower and fruit, while the male controlled the general habit, the types of leaves and other external features. As Sachs has pointed out (*70*, p. 87–8) this theory had an *a priori* origin, and was used to justify the Linnaean method of classification. But, since his systematics was so successful, many botanists came to accept all Linnaeus' theoretical premises along with his methods. Linnaeus and his disciples also used this sexual theory in developing their ideas on the hybrid origin of existing species. Since this aspect of their work attracted quite a lot of attention, this theory must have been widely known.

Koelreuter, whose monographs on plant breeding appeared at various times between 1761 and 1766 (*43*), started his work as an investigation into plant fertilisation. After examining the pollen and the stigmatic surfaces of many plants he became convinced that all pollen grains contain oil, and that the stigmas exude a similar fluid. As a result Koelreuter developed a completely different sexual theory, which was almost quasi-chemical. Throughout all nature there were two opposing 'principles': in the inorganic world there were the 'sulphuric' and the 'mercurial' principles which would, if mixed, combine to form a stable salt. In plants the male element represented the 'sulphur' and the female the 'mercury'. The production of a new individual was analogous to the formation of a salt, and the principles again separated out when the sex elements formed. Normally the same kind of elements combined to form each new generation of a plant type, and hence the species was preserved. But, just as it is possible to produce an impure salt by adding to a standard mixture a little of a slightly different 'sulphur' or 'mercury', so Koelreuter suggested that, in an analogous way, it might be possible to produce an 'impure' type of plant by introducing a little pollen or stigmatic juice from an allied variety during fertilisation.

Koelreuter did a number of experiments to demonstrate his sexual theory, but he later abandoned this interest and concentrated his attention on the artificial production of true hybrids between species. He disagreed with Linnaeus, inter-specific hybrids could never give rise to new species. He claimed that, in fact, such hybrids would never occur under natural conditions although they might be produced in botanical gardens or as the result of artificial pollination. Most of these hybrids would be infertile but, if they were fertile, their progeny would tend to revert to the original parental types (*43*, and *66*, p. 47). To demonstrate this he undertook a long series of experiments with a variety of plants and eventually produced a number of hybrids within the Nicotinia group. This work attracted the attention of his contemporaries, and it is plain, in retrospect, that he was one of the first of a long line of plant hybridists whose work culminated in Mendel's discoveries. His ideas on fertilisation, however, made little impression and were politely ignored by those who commented on his other results.

In general, then, by the middle of the eighteenth century the whole subject of vital organisation and of generation was again in chaos. Some, especially the doctors, still accepted one or other version of preformation. Animalculism was somewhat on the decline, and the ovist version seemed to be increasing in popularity amongst this group. Maupertuis' theory was more or less completely ignored and the more enthusiastic of the 'corpuscular' philosophers tended towards some variant of Buffon's views. But if these were to be accepted in the sense in which Buffon probably intended them, the explanatory power of his theory was minimal. If, on the other hand, this theory were modified to give a satisfactory explanation, then it almost certainly degenerated into an unscientific and extremely speculative form of vitalism. It was this latter which was beginning to be popular, especially amongst the intellectual *avant-garde* in France.

8

Wolff's Embryological Work

'We may conclude that the organs of the body have not always existed but have been formed successively; no matter how this formation has been brought about. I do not say that it has been brought about by a fortuitous combination of particles, by a kind of fermentation, through mechanical causes or through the activity of the soul, but only that it has been brought about.'

C. F. Wolff, THEORIA GENERATIONIS, 1759

THE eighteenth century scientists, such as Maupertuis, Buffon and Needham, who supported the various particulate theories of living matter, had opposed the preformation theory on a variety of grounds. Amongst other reasons, they always claimed that their theories were in better accord with the facts of embryo development; however, none of these workers was specifically interested in embryology. But almost simultaneously with their attack on the established theory, another attack was launched by the young German scientist, Casper Wolff, who was exclusively concerned with the facts of the development of plants and animals.

Wolff was one of the first naturalists to be influenced by that outlook which was later to be called Nature-Philosophy, for he was a disciple of Christian Wolff and an admirer of Stahl—both thinkers who helped to frame this philosophy. Christian Wolff (1679–1754) was a friend and admirer of Leibnitz. He taught philosophy and mathematics in Marburg and Halle, and though he made some contributions to botany he is best known as a philosopher. He stressed Leibniz's idea of pre-established harmony and denied that there were any causal connections in the world. All apparent interconnections between events were illusory. Change was due to the inner nature of things which developed according to predetermined laws. According to this school, which became very influential in the early nineteenth century, any attempt to explain living things in mechanical or physio-chemical terms was not just unsuccessful—it was misguided and irrelevant. It showed, they thought, a complete misunderstanding of the type of explanation which was required. The various forms of life were the manifestations of a single vital power or soul which acted within matter, and a knowledge of the gradual development of the different *forms* which were produced was itself an understanding of life.

The whole idea of attempting to give a causal or mechnical account of development was regarded as absurd. The majority of these thinkers were not scientists although, as we shall see in Chapter 13, they ultimately had a great effect on the development of nineteenth century biology. Many despised the mechanical sciences which had developed during the seventeenth and eighteenth centuries. They objected to the 'Newtonian' outlook and thought it essentially wrong-headed because it attempted to apply to nature a completely misleading model. Nature was *not* analogous to a machine, a subjective understanding of growth, development and change was the means by which all aspects of the Universe were to be understood. Their interest was in man himself, in his moral, intellectual and religious outlook and in the different types of societies and political institutions in which he lived. These they sought to explain in terms of biological growth. To reverse the process and demand a mechanical explanation from their central model would have been completely inconsistent.

Just how far Casper Wolff's outlook was completely that of a typical nature-philosopher is difficult to determine. He certainly shared Stahl's dislike for 'mechanical medicine'. But the introductory sections of his first work *Theoria Generationis* (99), which gave his theoretical views, are written in vague and obscure Latin, later translated into German by Wolff himself, and it is not always clear that the meaning attributed to these writings today would be that which Wolff intended. The *Theoria Generationis* started with a series of definitions. Thus 'generation' was defined as the formation of a body by the creation of its parts. Wolff claimed that to give a true explanation of a living thing one must show how the parts are formed, under the influence of the *vis essentialis*, acting according to certain principles.

According to Wolff these principles were nutrition, followed by growth and then differentiation.

Wolff wished to demonstrate his principles by considering the development of the stems of plants and the embryos of chicks. His choice of material suggests that he was concerned with the appearance of vital organisation, and was not interested in the nature of fertilisation. In fact, he did not discuss the origin of the chick from the parent, and said merely that reproduction was always a sign that nutrition was poor and that individual growth was waning.

His microscopic investigations were, of course, hampered by the poor definition of eighteenth century instruments. Without stains he could see no detail in the growing tissue, and, even in the plant material, cell differentiation had progressed some way before he actually saw the cells. Since he could make out more detail in the stems than in the embryos, much of what he says about the latter is a mere application of his discoveries about the former.

He came to the conclusion that at first a liquid drawn up from the soil collected at the growing point of the stem, where it formed a thin, homogeneous kind of jelly. As a result of evaporation, small sacs or vesicles were formed in this jelly, and fresh liquid collected within them. At first these vesicles were separated from each other by the original jelly, but gradually more and more of the sacs appeared in the interstices, until the whole was simply a solid mass of them, and most of the original jelly had been converted into vesicle walls. The ducts of the vascular system were formed by the sap hollowing out tracts in this mass, and at the same time some of the remaining jelly formed into new vesicles, which increased the girth of the stem.

Applying to the chick embryo what he had seen in plants, Wolff claimed that the initial jelly-like liquid was derived from the yolk, and formed two plates or lamina in which, as in the plant, vesicles appeared. Eventually, the embryo consisted of masses of these little sacs, in which no other structures could be seen. These then formed the heart and the vascular system in the same way as they produced the vessels in plants. Because he wished to emphasise the similarity between plant and animal development, Wolff directed his attention to the formation of the intestines, the blood vessels and the kidneys—parts whose final structures were clearly tubular, and where his interpretation, erroneous as it was, had most plausibility.

The vesicles or sacs which Wolff saw were cells. He was not the first to see them—Hooke had seen at least their remains, in cork, some hundred years before. But Wolff was the first to state that, at an early stage, both plants and animals consist of such elements. In assessing this, it must be remembered that Wolff's vesicles arose as secondary structures from within an undifferentiated mass of jelly, so that he was still a long way from the formulation of the modern cell theory. However, he did seem to believe that the mass of vesicles could change into other parts, for he remarked at one stage:

> The cellular substance, however, which surrounds the vertebral column and adjacent parts, furnishes the raw material for the elevation which will be structurally organised later. There can be no doubt about this for one who himself has observed the successive transformations of this substance. (*37*, p. 372)

Wolff here spoke of 'cellular substance', the German translation gives this the name 'Zell Substanz' although it refers to the vesicles as 'Kuegelchen'. By this time it was generally recognised that organs were composed of different kinds of fabric or tissue which could be classified into general types; thus Haller, Bonnet and other late eighteenth century biologists often speak of 'cellular tissue', 'osseous tissue', 'cartilaginous tissue', etc. But these terms were used in a purely descriptive manner: in particular, the phrase 'cellular tissue' meant nothing more than that the material had a certain appearance. For Wolff, this is not so. His 'cellular substance', whether it be found in the developing organism or in the adult, is formed from the mass of vesicles which have remained unchanged. In this respect he certainly made a big step towards a more complete understanding of vital organisation and its origins.

In the *Theoria Generationis* Wolff concentrated his attention on the early stages of the development of the chick. He gave an account of the spread of the blastoderm over the yolk, the appearance of the primitive streak and the formation of the mesoblastic somites. He described the early stages of the development of the blood system and the subsequent changes in the matter in the yolk. In 1768 and 1769, while living in Russia, he published a second work on the chick embryo, entitled *De Formatione Intestinorum* (*101*). This contained the best account yet given of the formation of the intestines and traced their development from a fold on the vertical side of the embryonic plate.

Wolff's work reached a new level in descriptive embryology. The modern period can be said to have begun at this time, and no historian of biology could possibly deny the significance of Wolff's observations for the development of the cell theory. He was the first naturalist to claim that all plant and animal parts had, at an early stage, an identical composition. So, although his account of the origin of the elements was mistaken and his description of their initial transformation was vague and confused, he drew attention to an enormously important aspect of vital organisation and development. However, from the fact that an investigation is of great importance when viewed retrospectively, it does not follow that the work as it stands will or should convince contemporaries. Contemporary scientists can only judge the actual evidence produced, and will only be convinced if that is sufficient to overthrow their own theories.

In 1759 the *Theoria Generationis* was published, and Wolff, who was only twenty-six at the time, stated that his account of the development of the embryo should be sufficient to disprove the preformation theory. In actual fact, that theory had been unpopular throughout the major part of his life. It was probably still taught in some medical schools, but no influential biologist was in agreement with it. Bonnet had expressed no opinions on generation. Maupertuis (who died in 1759) had produced an alternative theory, and so had Buffon and Needham. Haller, who had also been opposed to preformation, may have been converted to the theory in 1758 or 1759, but Wolff was presumably unaware of this change of opinion, for he dedicated his own work to Haller. From 1759 onwards to the end of the century there was a complete swing back to preformation. Wolff not only failed to persuade the preformationists to change their opinions, he failed to prevent a reconversion to the theory.

At first sight this may seem strange. But if Wolff's observations and theories are viewed from the point of view of an eighteenth century preformationist, the matter is not so surprising. In Chapter 3 mention was made of two different ways in which the preformation theory could be understood. It might be thought of as a theory which was susceptible of direct confirmation or refutation, in the same way that Harvey's assumption of a connection between arteries and veins was susceptible of proof. In this form the preformation was something which might be seen—if microscopes and techniques improved. Malpighi's discoveries rendered this version implausible, almost at the same time as the theory was announced, but it is possible that some of the earlier naturalists, particularly if they were animalculists and were not interested in embryology, may have accepted this form of the theory.

As we shall see in later chapters, the late eighteenth century preformationists certainly did not accept anything as naive as this. For them the preformation was completely invisible, and it was inconceivable that it would ever be seen in the young embryo. In this form, the preformation became an explanatory entity which was accepted because it made sense of a large number of different observations. The fact that it was possible, with the aid of certain techniques, to see parts before they normally became visible, helped to make the assumptions of the theory more plausible—just as Brownian movement and the behaviour of gases in Wilson cloud-chambers help us to accept the atomic theory. Preformationists who accepted their theory in this sense could give fairly accurate accounts of the gradual development of any organism, without feeling that this in any way falsified the theory. In fact it was just this phenomenon that the theory served to explain.

Hence, although Haller disagreed with Wolff on minor points, he gave an essentially similar *description* of the chick's development. Both these descriptions were not unlike those given by Aristotle, Harvey and Malpighi. The late eighteenth century preformationists never disputed such facts. Thus Bonnet, writing a general report for the layman, described the development of the heart in a chick in the following way:

> But the heart (when first seen) seems to be without covering, and to be placed on the outside of the body. Instead of appearing in the form of a minute pyramidical mass, it bears the appearance of a semi-circle. The other viscera appear successively and range themselves after each other, round the living speck. We cannot as yet discover any general folding; all is transparent or nearly so, and we only perceive little by little those teguments which are appointed to cover all the parts.
> (*8*, e, and *37*, p. 377)

No wonder Haller could say of Wolff's observations:

> . . . I have indeed seen many of the phenomena which he describes, and it is certain that the heart seems to be formed out of a congealed humour and that the whole animal appears to have the same consistency.
> (*87*, b, p. 116)

Any comparison between the descriptions of the development of the organs as given by Wolff and by any other eighteenth century embryologist would show the same essential agreement as to these facts. Wolff could not, therefore, claim that this aspect of his work would make his contemporaries alter their opinions. In discussing the subject Wolff showed that his case rested on a different aspect:

> In general, one cannot well say that what is not accessible to our senses is therefore non-existent. Yet applied to these observations, the principle is more sophistic than true. *The particles of which all animal organs are composed, in their primordial condition, are spherules always discernible with a microscope of medium power of magnification.* How could one maintain that one is unable to see a body because of its smallness, when the parts of which it is composed are easily recognisable? No-body has yet discovered with the help of a stronger lens parts not also visible with the help of a weaker magnification. Either one cannot see them at all or they appear sufficiently large. Therefore, that the parts are hidden because of their smallness, and that they then only gradually come forth, is a fable.
> (*99*, No. 85, Section CLXVI, p. 1)

Wolff correctly insisted that it was these vesicles (spherules) which turned into parts.

> . . . the formation of a part and its organisation are not accomplished in the individual by one and the same act, so that a formed part would be *eo ipse* organised: rather a part is first formed and then organised.
> (*99*, No. 85, Section CCXL, p. 58)

But though Wolff's observation and interpretation were, in fact, correct, even here it was the interpretation and not the observation which was new. Swammerdam (1672) had reported that as the tadpole started to grow, it first appeared as a pair of 'dumplings' (the two-cell stage of the zygote). Haller had also seen, before he could see any traces of the organs, the homogeneous jelly which took on a honeycomb appearance. He, however, interpreted the latter as a stage in the solidification of the parts. Thus, in reply to Wolff's observations he said:

> On the contrary, it is the removal of transparency and the accession of firmness to the extremities which gives a more obvious boundary to the contours of the viscera, and enable one to see the structure of the cellular

tissus (cellulosae telae). Wetness and transparency had previously hidden all these outlines.
(*87*, b, p. 116)

Thus both Wolff and the preformationists were in substantial agreement on what was actually seen under the microscope (Wolff and Haller did disagree on a minor point of observation, which they used as a test case. Even here, however, the disagreement was mainly a dispute about interpretations, see Chapter 9): what was at stake was interpretation and, above all, explanation. According to Wolff's interpretation the homogeneous primordia had no structure and the parts became visible at the moment they did because they were formed at that moment. According to the preformationists the same initial cellular appearance and subsequent gradual appearance of parts was all the result of an increase in size and solidity, which simply made apparent the pre-existent delineations. Just how acceptable Wolff's interpretation would be depended on the explanation he could offer for the facts he claimed.

Wolff spoke of certain principles—nutrition, growth and differentiation—and of the *vis essentialis* (wesentliche Kraft). 'Vis' is a vague word which can be translated into the following English words: 'strength', 'force', 'power', 'energy', 'virtue', 'essence' and 'mental strength'. Just what Wolff meant by the *vis essentialis* is therefore open to question. There seem at least three possibilities which suggest very different theories.

1 *Vis essentialis* = essential force. Wolff had in mind a force analogous to the forces in physics, and was suggesting that such a force acted as a causal agent to bring about the formation of the organism. The eighteenth century preformationists took Wolff to mean this, and objected that it was inconceivable that a single force would be equal to this task. Bonnet referred to Wolff's 'curious system' in a footnote, and argued against this idea:

All force is indeterminate and cannot of itself produce specific efforts, or in other words it presupposes the existence of the mechanism which it activates. If, therefore, there is nothing preformed in the matter which the essential force is supposed to organise, how can that force produce, let us say, an animal instead of a plant, a particular kind of animal, and a special set of organs of the arrangement and proportions appropriate to that animal.
(*8*, d, Part II, Chap. 7, Art. 345, pp. 437–8, footnote)

If Wolff meant the *vis essentialis* to be understood in this mechanical way the criticism is fully justified. He claimed that the material was at first a homogeneous jelly without any structure, and even if he allowed that each bit of jelly from a parent of a certain kind had a certain specific character, this would still be insufficient, for the reasons Bonnet gave. But, given Wolff's dislike of 'mechanical medicine', it seems extremely improbable that he intended the *vis essentialis* to be in any way mechanical.

2 *Vis essentialis*=an indwelling vital force, soul or entelechy. If this was what Wolff meant, then the explanation is not inadequate in the above way, although it would not be acceptable to the majority of the eighteenth century naturalists. The theory would be similar to many which had been given in the past, and somewhat like Turberville Needham's theory of 'vegetative force'. However, there is little evidence that Wolff did mean the *vis essentialis* to be thought of as an active causal agent, and this interpretation is inconsistent with some of his later remarks (see below). Moreover, according to Needham (*54*, p. 227), Blumenbach, who postulated a *nisus formativus* or formative force, said his postulated force differed from Wolff's *vis essentialis* because it did the active shaping, and did not simply control the addition of material.

3 *Vis essentialis*=essential nature. On this view Wolff was simply not interested in giving a *causal* explanation of the phenomena. He was influenced by philosophical views similar to those of the later nature-philosophers, who regarded development and differentiation as fundamental characteristics of the universe. Such 'philosophers' believed that this development followed a very general pattern, and the principles they looked for were the 'laws of development' descriptive of this pattern. They did not, moreover, seek causal explanations of successive changes, for they regarded change and development as a fundamental fact, and, as such, in need of no explanation. On this third view, then, Wolff was concerned to derive the 'formal' principles of development from his study of the phenomena. To put the difference in Aristotelian terms: construed in the second way the *vis essentialis* was a (spiritual) 'efficient cause' of developmental changes—construed in this third way it was the 'formal cause' of development. Having specified these—nutrition, growth and differentiation—he had done

all that was, on this view, required. This interpretation of Wolff would accord both with his philosophical background and with remarks like the following:

> We may conclude that the organs of the body have not always existed, but have been formed successively—no matter how this formation has been brought about. I do not say that it has been brought about by a fortuitous combination of particles, a kind of fermentation, through mechanical causes, through the activity of the soul, but only that it has been brought about.
> (*100*, p. 245 and *95*)

Wolff's acceptance of a view of this third sort would explain some rather curious aspects of his work. The general attitude of the nature-philosophers commonly resulted in an unfamiliar mixture of the extremely metaphysical and the extremely empirical, which is also a feature of Wolff's work.

If this was Wolff's position then he certainly differed from all his contemporaries in an extremely fundamental way. Most of the late eighteenth century naturalists were forced back to preformation because they insisted on a causal explanation for generation and refused to believe that events in the world were due to any causes other than those reducible to physics and chemistry. But Wolff could dispense with preformation, because he denied the need for causal explanation. The dispute between the preformationists and epigenesists was to be resolved as soon as the cell theory was established. The difficulty was to be shelved for those naturalists who altered their outlook and ceased to demand a causal explanation. Wolff contributed to the overthrow of preformation in both these ways: his investigations aided the establishment of the cell theory and he heralded a new non-mechanistic outlook on nature.

9

Haller—the First of the Late Eighteenth Century Preformationists

'If Harvey thought he described an epigenetic development, it was because he saw first a little cloud, then the rudiments of the head, with the eyes bigger than the whole body, and little by little viscera being formed. If one compares his description with mine, one will see that his description of the development of the deer corresponds exactly with mine of the development of the chick. If more than twenty years ago I too employed this reasoning . . . I have realised abundantly since that all I said against preformation really went to support it.'

Haller, ELEMENTA PHYSIOLOGIAE, 1766

DURING the period between 1730 and 1760 the preformation theory became progressively less popular. It would be reasonable to suppose that the new discoveries and new theories described in the last four chapters might have killed it completely. Yet it was just about 1760 that a new ovist version of preformation became popular, and maintained its popularity for over thirty or forty years. The three greatest and most influential biologists of the time—Haller, Bonnet and Spallanzani—were jointly responsible for this change of opinion. None of these men started out as preformationists and each became a convert when he was already well known and respected as a naturalist. The cumulative effect of these conversions was considerable. Each by supporting the theory encouraged the others to do likewise, and by presenting a united front they convinced most of their contemporaries.

Haller was the first to revive and reintroduce this new ovism, but he did not do so until about 1758, when he was over fifty years old and already one of the most famous scientists in Europe. A man of wide interest, a poet and botanist as well as a physiologist, he did not appear to be greatly interested in the problems of generation until about 1740, when he started to edit a posthumous collection of Boerhaave's lecture notes. Boerhaave, who taught earlier in the century, had tentatively accepted the animalculism which was then fashionable. Haller took the trouble to add a note to the lectures on generation, pointing out that the recent discoveries of animal regeneration made preformation untenable and that, in any case, it was incompatible with the facts of embryo development (*7*, Part II, p. 497). With respect to the latter point it must be remembered that it would be assumed in the eighteenth century that spermatozoa, if they were living animals, would have organs, and that if they gave rise to the foetus, it would be these same organs which developed into the corresponding animals or human parts. It is, therefore, more difficult to reconcile animalculism with the facts of embryo development than it is to reconcile ovism. In the former case, the organs must be completely formed in the motile and very vital spermatozoa; in the latter case, it is possible to imagine that the preformation is of a more rudimentary kind. It was always the animalculists who pressed the descriptive version of preformation, and they who suggested that the parts might be visible at conception. The ovists, on the other hand, could accept a less literal version of the theory, and could more easily regard the original preformation as an invisible phenomenon which accounted for the gradual appearance of the parts as the embryo developed. So far as I know, no biologist who made a special study of embryology was ever an animalculist, whereas many great embryologists, in the seventeenth and eighteenth centuries, were ovists.

It is not surprising that Haller opposed preformation in the period between 1740 and 1750. It was at this time that regeneration was attracting attention and that many alternative theories were suggested. Haller may have hoped that a satisfactory solution to the problems of generation might be found along the lines suggested by Maupertuis or Buffon. In 1751, however, Haller published a criticism of Buffon's system (*90*). It will be recalled that Buffon believed that organic matter was made up of vital particles which could form into various patterns and that within any individual the pattern was always identical. Haller replied by pointing out that living things varied, and that there were even individual variations in the formation of the same organs within any one species. No system such as Buffon's, which depended on something akin to geometric patterns, could possibly account for such diversities. About this time, Haller was obviously becoming more interested in generation, for he produced a collection of historical papers on important physiological topics, including a set on generation which gave a history of the subject during the previous sixty years (*91*).

Soon after this Haller started his own investigations into the development of the chick embryo, and his memoirs on the subject were read in 1757 to the Goettingen scientific society, and published the following year (*89*). In spite of the interest taken in various aspects of generation, relatively little work had been done in embryology during the eighteenth century. Perhaps Haller hoped that by re-examining this aspect of the subject he would be able to settle some of the current disputes. In fact this work convinced him of the truth of preformation and converted him to ovism. In addition, however, his actual work did open up new lines of enquiry. According to Needham 'it [Haller's embryological investigation] stands out, with that of his opponent Wolff, as the greatest between Malpighi and von Baer' (*54*, p. 193). He made much more use of various reagents to harden the parts and increase visibility. He also introduced a quantitative approach and pioneered the subject of the growth rate of developing organisms. He calculated the rate of growth of the chick and of the human embryo, and actually measured the increases in length and weight of the main bones in the chick embryo from the time of their first appearance until hatching.

In the course of his enquiries Haller noted the close connection between the yolk and the foetus in the chick. He observed that the blood vessels in the yolk were continuous with the embryonic blood system, and that 'the inner membrane of the yolk' (the endoderm) was continuous with the inner membrane of the intestines and with the skin. He apparently believed that the latter connection was present from the start and not, as is the case, only after the gut cavity has formed. Similarly he appeared to have had the mistaken belief that 'the skin which covers the yolk during the last days of incubation' (the allanto-chorion) was part of the foetal skin. Professor Cole, who unravelled Haller's observations, reinterpreted them in modern terms, and analysed his mistakes, has claimed that it was these which converted Haller to both preformation and ovism (*11*, pp. 88–9). Haller was certainly impressed by the close connection between the yolk and the foetus; these 'observations' play a part in the factual disagreements between him and Wolff, and are often referred to. But an examination of Haller's writings, and especially his treatment of the whole subject in the *Elementa Physiologiae*, suggests that he regarded them as important in settling the rival claims of the male and the female as the donor of the preformed embryo. His discussions of the interpretation of the chick were within the framework of the preformation theory, for they presupposed its acceptance. Professor Cole criticises Haller's argument on this point and claims that it contains premises such as 'the yolk is continuous with the skin and intestine, it must be contemporaneous with it' which beg the question and assume what he set out to prove (see Cole's footnote to page 88). These premises assume preformation but are neutral as to the animalculist or ovist version. If my interpretation is correct, Haller is perfectly justified in assuming them to argue to a new conclusion within the theory. He is, in fact, wrong, but is not guilty of the logical errors Cole ascribes to him. He might, with more justice, have suggested that it was these investigations which decided Haller in favour of the ovist version of the theory. Even this would be a little unfair, for Haller always gave three independent sets of reasons for his choice of the female as the origin of the foetus. These were:

1 The difficulties which were associated with the animalculist position (see below).

2 The close connection between the yolk and the foetus in the chick, as illustrated by his own investigations, from which Haller generalised via 'the analogies of nature' to a similar close connection in quadrupeds and other groups.

3 The existence of parthenogenesis within the female line amongst some animals, notably the aphids.

The following passages give the argument as it appeared in a later work by Haller (*88*, Chap. 35, pp. 457–8).

> To the father some have attributed everything; chiefly after the seminal worms, now so well-known, were first observed in the male seed with the help of the microscope, which are observed with truth to agree in figure with the first embryos of all animals. But in these animals there is wanting a proportion betwixt their number and that of the fetuses; they are also not to be observed constantly through all the different tribes of animals; they have too great a resemblance to those animalculae that are everywhere spontaneously produced in other parts of the body, which yet are always tenacious of their own genus, and are never found to grow in [into] the most different kind of animals that have limbs.

> Again, other anatomists not less celebrated or less worthy of credit, have taught that the fetus existed in the mother and maternal ovary; which the male semen excites into a more active life and likewise forms it variously so as to show it just brought into life and makes its presence manifest. Yolks are also manifestly found in the female ovaries, even although they have not been impregnated with any male semen. But a yolk is well-known to be an appendix to the intestine of fowls; and to have its arteries from the mesenteric artery and the covering of the yolk to be continued with the inner membrane of the intestines, which is continuous with the skin of the animal. Along with the yolk, therefore, the fetus seems to be present in the mother hen of whom the yolk is part, and which gives vessels to the yolk. Lastly, that the analogy of nature shows that many animals generate eggs without any connections with a male of the same species but that a male animal never becomes prolific without a female. That the progressions are continuous from the female quadruped to an oviparous animal, and from that to one which is not oviparous. But the young animal proceeds from a part of the old one from which it is generated. Certainly, therefore, the males must give some addition to that sex which produces the fetus from its own body; which addition is necessary in some tribes of animals but in others may be wanting . . .

These were Haller's reasons for preferring an ovist version of preformation rather than an animalculist version. His reasons for accepting the whole idea of preformation were more complicated.

Haller is famous as the author of a very comprehensive textbook, in eight volumes, *Elementa Physiologiae* (1766) which contained summaries of all recent advances in the subject. The work was translated and abridged, and was used through the medical schools of Europe. In the section 'On the Foetus' in the original text, Haller gave a survey of all the recent discoveries which might be important for the understanding of generation, and discussed many of the theoretical points involved. It seems clear from this discussion that there was no single fact which he regarded as settling the issue for or against preformation, and that he was convinced rather on a balance of probabilities. Some of the considerations which inclined him towards preformation were of a general nature and others were more specific; some were positive merits of the theory and others were deficiencies he saw in rival views. Many of the difficulties which led to the original formulation of the preformation theory still remained—increased, not diminished, by the accumulation of new knowledge. None of the investigations of the proceeding century had suggested that there were living creatures that lacked organs. There was, as yet, no knowledge of the structure of the microscopic creatures seen by Leeuwenhoek; and although it was gradually becoming evident that some animals, such as the polyps and volvox, had a much simpler structure than the higher animals, it was clear that even the polyps had parts, including a stomach. Hence the idea that anything could be a living independent unit while bereft of organic structure still lacked empirical backing, and the embryo, if indeed it lacked organs, was as great, or even a greater anomaly, than it had appeared in the seventeenth century.

As a physiologist, Haller was well aware of the close connection and interdependence of the different organs, and knew of no evidence to support the idea that any organ or system could function without the others being present. To any biologist who thought of the body as a system of organs, the gradual appearance in a living individual of heart and blood system, brain and nerves, of the eyes and other sense organs, presented an enormous puzzle—that something could exist without at least a rudimentary heart, etc., was an impossibility. Haller was prepared to allow that the young heart had a very different form from the adult one, and that the arteries arose and grew from different points much as Wolff had described, but considerations such as the foregoing compelled him to maintain that each part was present in a rudimentary form within the youngest embryo. It was the impossibility of reconciling the unity of the organism with epigenesis which forced Haller to accept preformation. The following statement gives his conclusions and, perhaps, implies something of his reasoning:

> In the body of the animal therefore, no part is made before any other part, but all are formed at the same time. If certain authors have said that the animal begins to be formed by the backbone, by the brain or by the heart, if Galen taught that it was the liver which was first formed, if others have said that it was the belly and the head, or the spinal marrow with the brain, adding that these parts make others in turn; I think that all these authors only meant that the heart and the brain or whatever organ it was, were visible when none of the other parts yet were, and that certain parts of the embryonic body are well enough developed in the first few days to be seen while others are not so until the latter part of development; and others again not till after birth, such as the beard in man, the antlers in the stag, the breasts and the second set of teeth. If Harvey thought he described an epigenetic development, it was because he saw first a little cloud, then the rudiments of the head, with the eyes bigger than the whole body and little by little

viscera being found. If one compares his description with mine, one will see that his descriptions of the development of the deer corresponds exactly with mine of the development of the chick. If more than twenty years ago, before I had made many observations upon eggs and the females of quadrupeds, I employed this reasoning to prove that there is a great difference between the fetus and the perfect animal, and if I said that in the animal at the moment of conception one does not find the same parts as in the perfect animal, I have realised abundantly since then that all I said against preformation really went to support it.
(*87*, b, p. 148)

Swammerdam's use of new techniques had enabled him to see the parts of the adult insect in the pupa, at a time when these were invisible to the naked eye—it was this which helped to convince him of the truth of preformation. Haller's more extensive use of acetic acid in embryological research had the same effect. In the course of a discussion of Wolff's work, he put the matter in the following way:

. . . I have indeed seen many of the phenomena which he [Wolff] describes and it is certain that the heart seems to be formed out of a congealed humour and that the whole animal appears to have the same consistency. But it does not follow that because this primitive glue, which is to take on the shape of the animal, does not appear to possess structure and all its parts, that it has not effectively got them. *I have often given a greater solidity to this jelly by the use merely of spirits of lime, and by this means I say that what appeared to me to be a homogeneous jelly was composed of fibres, vessels and viscera.*
(*87*, a, p. 116)

Haller's previous concern with Buffon's work suggests that at the start of his own investigations he was already interested in attempts to provide a causal explanation for reproduction and embryo growth. As an eighteenth century man, for whom the triumphs of physics had set the pattern of scientific success, he would be dissatisfied with anything less than a complete explanatory system. Nor would he expect this to be an impossibility—Newton's success had not only set a pattern, it had also led to a general optimism about all scientific matters, which was only gradually seen to be misplaced. The vitalism of Aristotle was dead, Stahl's views had made little impression, and the vitalism of the German romantics had not yet begun to influence biology. Haller was able to state, as something too obvious to need discussion:

> . . . the soul is certainly an architect unequal to the task of producing such a beautiful fabric.
> (*88*, Chap. 21, p. 459)

Eschewing all forms of vitalism, Haller was left with either preformation or with a solution along the lines suggested by Maupertuis or Buffon. On the purely theoretical side all solutions, except preformation, included the idea of a 'force', acting according to discoverable and presumably uniform laws, which was ultimately responsible for the organisations of the body. Too much was required of these 'forces', and too little could be said about them. We may admire some of the brilliant insights shown by Buffon or by Maupertuis, because we can see that by arguing from crucial facts they did reach conclusions which were to get partial confirmation from subsequent research. But against the background knowledge of the time Haller had justification for the following remark:

> As for the 'internal moulds' of which I could never conceive one clear idea in my mind, we shall refer them to those hypotheses which the desire, of explaining things of which we are unwillingly ignorant, has given rise.
> (*88*, Chap. 21, p. 459)

Not only did these alternative theories involve the assumption of a force for which it was difficult to give an analogy; they also involved the assumption of particles for which there was no evidence. The use of re-agents seemed to give some plausibility to the assumption of a preformation, but there was no way in which the particles could be seen.

In order to account for the bi-parental effects on the offspring, Needham, Buffon and Maupertuis had been forced to assume that both sexes produced secretions and that these intermingled in the uterus. Buffon claimed to have discovered 'spermatozoa-like' structures in the Graafian follicles, but nobody accepted this. Needham's theory depended on his belief in spontaneous generation, and on his experiments with the corked phials of hot broth. Haller dismissed spontaneous generation on the evidence of Redi, Swammerdam and Leeuwenhoek; he was suspicious of Needham's results, even before Spallanzani disproved them. Maupertuis denied that the Graafian follicles played any part in generation and returned to the idea of a female secretion from the uterus itself. Each of these theories, then, involved the assumption of some factual matter directly contrary to accepted experience.

Haller always allowed that the subject of generation could be considered from many points of view, but as a physiologist he gave more weight to the considerations discussed above, and less to the facts of regeneration and to heredity. Although he became a convert to preformation, convinced that none of the other hypotheses would account so well for the orderly series of changes he had observed in the developing embryo, his support was always qualified. Whenever he discussed the matter he always pointed out that children did resemble both parents, and that the facts of inheritance and hybrid formation did not fit in well with the theory. In the *Elementa Physiologiae* the longest account of inheritance followed the section in which Haller discussed and concurred with the ovist version of preformation. In this section Haller commenced with the statement:

> Although this hypothesis [the ovist version of preformation] shines forth with the happy appearance of truth and seems to be very compatible with nature, it should not be adopted immediately. It is certain, no matter how much you are attracted to it, that there is a difficulty from which one can not easily escape.
> (*87*, Bk. 29, Section II, Chap. 8, p. 96)

The difficulty is, of course, that the offspring may resemble either parent, and that it certainly does not inherit from the mother alone, as the theory would suggest. Haller summarised what was known of inheritance in man and in animals. He mentioned Réaumur's study of polydactyly, and much of Maupertuis' work, including his experiments with the Icelandic dogs, but most of the examples are clearly taken from medical literature, and are based on mere anecdotes. He included a long list of hybrids reported by writers from classical times onwards—a list which contained reports of crosses between horses and cattle, asses and cattle, sheep and goats, women and apes and a cat and a rat, as well as more plausible cases of crosses between angora and ordinary goats, wolves and dogs, and lions and tigers. It is quite clear from the account that it had long been the practice to account for monsters and abnormal offspring by supposing that the parents had had intercourse with some other type of animal. Haller, although he apparently felt it necessary to include these reports, was plainly sceptical of them, but lacked any means of deciding between the reliable and unreliable cases.

In most of the examples little detailed description was given of the progeny, but certain characters were occasionally mentioned. The offspring of a common she goat and a male angora, for instance, were reported to be all long haired, but the reciprocal case between a male short hair and a female angora was said to yield some long and some short-haired offspring. The identity of reciprocal crosses with respect to any single character had not been noticed, though Koelreuter had noted a similarity between the reciprocal crosses in a tobacco hybrid but did not specify an identity with respect to any particular character. This was not surprising, since there was no theroetical reason for looking at heredity from the point of view of single characters. Moreover in the best-known hybrids—the crosses between donkeys and horses—the mule and the hinny were always distinguished and described as very different animals.

From the data he cited Haller concluded that the offspring might resemble either parent, or even grandparent. He thought that, in humans, the child seemed to derive more from the mother and that the general health of the child depended more on this parent. On the other hand he added a list of diseases and deformities which were known to have been passed from the father to a child. He obviously found all the evidence very conflicting, for he went on to draw attention to some items which he found particularly puzzling. These included the following facts:

(a) Some diseases and deformities were clearly transmitted from one generation to the next, since they occurred again and again in the same family (cf. studies of polydactyly).

(b) Nevertheless similar deformities seem to appear suddenly in the offspring of normal parent (the case cited is that of prize mares who sometimes give birth to maimed, blind or deformed offspring).

(c) Maimed, deformed and sick parents can, on the other hand, produce healthy offspring.

(d) The same woman may bring forth some children like herself and some like the father.

Although the evidence was still very scanty, Haller was beginning to see that it could not be generalised in terms of parental donations: inheritance was obviously a very complicated subject which raised a host of unanswered questions.

10

Charles Bonnet

'I understand in general by the word germ every pre-ordination, every preformation of parts capable by itself of determining the existence of a Plant or an Animal.'

Charles Bonnet, CONTEMPLATION DE LA NATURE, 1764

CHARLES BONNET, the next naturalist to announce his conversion to preformation, became well known at the early age of twenty-two, when he confirmed Réaumur's idea that the aphids must sometimes reproduce without intercourse with the male. This work on parthenogenesis, done in 1742, was a model piece of research—careful, systematic and well described (*8*, a). Soon afterwards, excited by his relation Trembley's discoveries, Bonnet started enquiries into regeneration in various worms. These established that the phenomenon occurred in this group, but did not lead to any generalisations of the kind he hoped to discover. The result of this early work was published in 1744 in the *Traité d'Insectologie*, and for the next ten or fifteen years Bonnet continued to work on the anatomy and physiology of the lower animals (*8*, b). Later he turned his attention to botanical topics and investigated the interchange of air and water through the leaves (*8*, c). Throughout this period Bonnet showed little interest in theoretical questions and none in the problem of generation. His work is remarkable for its Baconian approach—a great number of experiments are described in detail, but few conclusions are drawn.

Unfortunately, Bonnet's eyesight began to fail and he was unable to continue with this type of research. He, therefore, turned his attention to the more theoretical aspects of biology and, in 1762, published his *Considérations sur les Corps Organisés* (*8*, d) in which he announced his conversion to preformation. He claimed in the preface that he actually wrote part of the manuscript some fifteen years before, at a time when he was drawn towards ovism, but did not think that the embryological facts supported it. When, in 1758, Haller published the results of his work on the chick embryo and independently arrived at the same theory, Bonnet felt justified in publishing his essay. But he still offered it as a mere hypothesis, with the following methodological comment and excuse:

> One cannot have too many conjectures on an obscure subject. . . . Conjectures act as sparks which may kindle a torch that can lead the way to new experiments. So while I can praise the timidity of some physicians who simply stick to the facts, I cannot condemn the ingenious rashness of those who sometimes attempt to penetrate beyond them. Let us look in all directions, form new conjectures and give birth to new hypotheses, but let us always remember that they are but conjectures and hypotheses and never put them in the place of facts.
> (*8*, d, Chap. 3, Art. XXIV, p. 99)

Since he never removed this remark from the text one must assume that he would, if pressed, have always held that his theory was a mere hypothesis.

Nevertheless, from 1762 until his death in 1793, he devoted himself entirely to developing the idea of preformation and constructing a vast scientific and metaphysical system upon it. During this time he wrote a large number of essays, which were eventually collected together and published (*8*, vols. I–X), to be edited and re-edited by the author who added, to each new edition, new footnotes recording recent discoveries or indicating changes in his views. Professor Whitman examined the whole system in a series of lectures given in 1894 (*96*), and more recently Professor Bentley Glass has discussed it in an essay entitled *Heredity and Variation in the Eighteenth Century Concept of the Species* (*33*, p. 164 ff.). Both these works give excellent accounts of Bonnet's general ideas. I shall concentrate on his ideas on preformation and generation, and shall try to show how Bonnet modified the basic theory in order to include all the new discoveries made in the eighteenth century.

Since Bonnet's whole cosmic system was based on preformation, he returned to the topic many times in the *Considérations*, in the *Contemplation de la Nature* (1764), in the *Palingénésie* (1769), and in many minor works. In spite of a scattered presentation, and of the different times at which the accounts were written, they are remarkably consistent. Minor alterations do occur, called for by new evidence or by reconsideration of specific points, but the fundamental assumptions remain unchanged. Every topic is treated with logical precision, and ideas implicit in other writings become for the first time explicit, as Bonnet gives them minute attention. A love of detail, evident in the early works, compels him to consider every aspect, so the theory at last becomes complete and truly systematic.

The title of the first essay on the subject, *Considérations sur les Corps Organisés*, makes it clear that Bonnet, like most eighteenth century naturalists, regarded the possession of a structure of organised parts as a necessary condition for life. He was deeply impressed by the harmony between these parts in all living things, and by the correlation between structure and mode of life. He argued, in the familiar way, that the parts could not function independently, and that if the young embryo was truly living it must possess in some rudimentary form the relevant organs. In spite of, or perhaps because of, his religious convictions, Bonnet would have no mysterious vital forces at work in nature—the cosmos, once created, must function according to physical and chemical laws. Hence scientific (i.e. true) explanations must be mechnical. Yet no mechanical force seemed sufficient to form, in each individual, the observable structures.

> All force is indeterminate and cannot of itself produce specific effects, or in other words it presupposes the existence of the mechanism which it activates. If, therefore, there is nothing preformed in the matter which the essential force is supposed to organise, how can that force produce, let us say, an animal instead of a plant, a particular kind of animal, and a special organ appropriate to that animal?
> (*8*, d, Part II, Chap. 7, pp. 437–8, footnote)

Preformation is the best hypothesis, he thinks, since it avoids all these difficulties.

> A true philosopher would not undertake to explain mechanically the formation of a head or an arm, however simple might be the structure of this head or this arm. In the most simple organic structure there are still so many relations, these relations are so varied, so direct; all the parts are so intimately connected, so dependent on one another, so co-operative to the same end, that they could not be conceived of as having been formed one

after the other and arrayed successively, like molecules of a salt or a crystal. A sound philosopher has eyes that discover in every organised body the ineffaceable imprint of a work done at a single stroke, and which is the expression of that Adorable Will that said 'Let organic bodies be' and they were. They were from the beginning, and their first appearance is what we very improperly call generation, birth.
(*8*, e, Part IX, Chap. 1, p. 2 and *96*, p. 238)

The assumption of preformation by itself tells us nothing of the form or the subsequent distribution of animate matter. It could be that the preformed units have floated around in the air, earth and water ever since creation, and that they always mature when suitable conditions prevail. Plainly this is not the case, and Bonnet is convinced that there is no 'spontaneous generation'. The germs of future generations of all types of animate matter have, he thinks, always been within the bodies of the living—life only comes from life. He points out that in all the doubtful cases yet examined this rule has been found to hold. He cites the researches of Redi, Réaumur and Swammerdam, and insists that it will be found to be true of the infusoria, in spite of Needham's conclusions. When Spallanzani announced the results of his work, Bonnet was naturally delighted and added a précis of them in a footnote to the *Considérations* (*8*, d, Part II, Chap. 6, pp. 286–317, footnote, pp. 317–39).

The assumption of preformation likewise tells us nothing by itself about the form of the germ. It could be that each germ was a unique construction, and that there were as many kinds of germs as there were individuals. But plainly, again this is not so—we can speak of kinds or species. In the *Considérations* Bonnet appears to hold that, for any species, God created more or less identical germs—it is this which preserved the similarity of form from one generation to the next. He says when discussing the mule:

This production exists, but in the form of a horse, in the ovaries of the mare.
(*8*, d, Part I, Chap. 3, p. 109)

When discussing inheritance in man he became even more explicit:

But let us admit that all human germs have been created with five digits on the hands and feet—or, which comes to the same thing—that there is but one species (éspèce) of man.
(*8*, d, Part II, Chap. 8, footnote, p. 499)

In his later works, when taking a cosmic view, Bonnet modified his opinion on this point, but in a way which did not really affect his ideas on generation.

Earlier it had been noted that preformation itself did not entail that the germs in any species were identical. When speaking of generation in the *Considérations* Bonnet assumed that they were, at least, very similar. When speculating about the past history and future destiny of living things, Bonnet did allow for a gradual change over long periods of time. He was convinced, partly on fossil evidence, that there have been, and will be, catastrophes which destroy all living bodies, leaving only the germs to carry on life. Moreover he hopefully believed that all living things will attain a sort of salvation. In his later view he envisaged the germs of one species as a series gradually attaining higher levels of organisation. Seen from the short-term point of view of human experience the series is practically unchanging: seen against a long period of time the series changes. Men will become angels, apes human, and all will gradually move up the Great Chain of Being. This sounds like evolution, but it is not achieved by any gradual improvement from within, nor by the action of any external conditions. It is simply the unfolding of preformed germs, made on this plan by the Benevolent Creator. This theory is discussed in the *Palingénésie*. (For further details see the articles by Bentley Glass and Whitman, *31* and *95*.)

As a result of the various studies of animal regeneration, some naturalists, including Buffon, Wolff and Bonnet, were beginning to see that all growth, both animal and vegetable, had much in common. From the earlier concentration on sexual reproduction in animals, interest widened to include the equivalent process in plants, and all forms of asexual reproduction and regeneration. Bonnet had a general theory which covered all these cases. All started as germs, which contained the primordia of the mature structures. The subsequent increase in size, and the gradual change of form in the parts, was brought about by the intake of inorganic material. God had created the structures; everything else was the result of chemical or physical processes, rather like the intake of water in a dry rubber sponge.

> I pictured the germ as a network, the elements of which formed the meshes. The nutritive molecules, incorporating themselves into these meshes, tended to enlarge them. . . .

I conceived the elements of the germ as the primordial foundation, on which the nutritive molecules went to work to increase in every direction the dimensions of the parts.

Strictly speaking, I said [Art. 83, pp. 47, 48], the elements [inorganic] do not form organic bodies, they only develop them, and this is accomplished by nutrition. The primitive organisation of the germs determines the arrangement which the nourishing atoms must take in order to become parts of the organic whole.
(*8*, f, Part VIII, Chap. 4, p. 205 and *96*, p. 246)

Thus, though for Bonnet there was no formation of organic structures, and though organic forms could never be developed from inorganic matter, physical and chemical processes did nevertheless play an important role.

Bonnet believed that all vital processes were of this kind, and that the inorganic nutritive material could effect profound alterations in the developing germs. In fertilisation the semen must come into contact with the egg; but the semen was normally essential, simply because it provided the best possible food for the developing germ. Fertilisation introduced no new organic structure—the germ had already got the primordia of all the adult structures—it was a physio-chemical process which stimulated growth and provided the necessary conditions for it. In animals which reproduce by parthenogenesis the female happened to be able to provide these conditions, just as they can be provided in asexual reproduction and in regeneration. Since the semen merely provided the right food and stimulated the heart, it might be possible to replace it by another chemical—a matter on which Spallanzani later conducted some interesting, if unsuccessful, experiments.

The distribution of the germs within living bodies, and the actual character of the germs, were both secondary matters to Bonnet. He believed that in sexually reproducing animals the germs collected in the female ovaries. He accepted ovism for the usual reasons: the case against animalculism was strong, this version of preformation seemed to agree best with the facts of embryo development, and parthenogenesis occurred only in female animals. He was not concerned with preformation in any descriptive sense; it was purely an explanation for the gradual appearance of the parts, and the germs were not in any sense miniature adult animals. Bonnet quoted, with approval, the accounts of embryo development given by Harvey and Malpighi.

Because his eyesight failed before he could make any observations on embryos he had to rely on the works of others and, naturally, accepted Haller's description of the development of the chick, rather than Wolff's. Even here, however, his principal criticism was not that Wolff's facts were incorrect, but that his inference to a formative *vis essentialis* was wrong. In the quotation given above Bonnet speaks of the germ as a 'network' containing 'the elements of all the organic parts'. Elsewhere he made it clear that he believed that the young embryo was made of a fluid and transparent jelly-like substance, in which no structure could be seen. Even if it were possible to see the young animal at this stage, it would in no way resemble the adult form.

> Whilst the chick is still in the form of a germ all its parts have a form, proportion and position which differ considerably from those they will ultimately assume. Consequently if we enlarge it at this stage it would not be possible to recognise it as a chick.
> (*8*, d, Part II, Chap. 7, Art. 351, p. 461)

Occasionally when discussing other topics Bonnet does speak of the germ as a 'miniature animal' (see above). At first sight this seems to be a contradiction, but closer examination of the text makes it clear that in these cases Bonnet is speaking figuratively, and wishes to remind the reader, in the briefest possible way, that the germ contains the elements or primordia of an unequivocal and specific type of animal.

Since many plants and some animals can be reproduced from cuttings, Bonnet inferred that in these cases the germs must also be spread widely throughout the fabric of the body. Thus, the hydra must contain germs in all parts of its anatomy, since minute portions can regenerate whole animals. Whenever a new part is regenerated, a germ must have initiated that growth. Bonnet had some difficulty with these cases. So far he had assumed that each germ contained the rudiments of the whole organism, but in most cases of regeneration it is only the appropriate part which is re-formed, e.g. the tadpole grows a new tail if the first is amputated, the crayfish develops a new claw to replace a lost one. In these cases, was the germ responsible, the germ of the whole organism, only part of which develops, or was it a germ which contained rudiments of the lost part only? Bonnet discussed the matter in detail and inclined to the latter view (*8*, d, Part II, Chap. I, Art. 254–7).

Preformation itself will explain the continuity of type from one generation to the next, the unity between the parts of an organism and the orderly differentiation which is always observed when a new individual or part develops—whether it be a foetus, the result of non-sexual reproduction or merely a regeneration. But from the assumption of preformation alone, one might expect there would be no variations between individuals of a given species; yet variation is so general that no biologist can deny it. In the preceding decades it had been the grosser forms of variation, the 'monsters', the hybrids and the individuals who inherited anomalous characteristics, which had always been cited as incompatible with the theory. No eighteenth century theoretician could hope that his theory would be successful unless he could deal with these objections. Even in Bonnet's original theory his ideas on nutrition provided the basis for an explanation of variation. He always emphasised that nutrition could alter the character of an organism within certain limits, and pointed to the power of madder to colour the bones of animals who fed on it (*8*, d, Part I, Chap. 3, Art. 34, p. 105) and to certain herbs which cause the cows to give flavoured milk. In general, it is the differences in the food, especially in the early stages, and the differences in the environment which account for individual characteristics.

> The germ carries the original imprint of the species. It is a miniature man, a horse, or bull, etc. but it is not a *certain* man, a *certain* horse, a *certain* bull, etc. All the germs are contemporaneous in the system of *emboîtement*. The characteristics are not transmitted from one to another. I do not say all members are exactly similar. I see nothing of identity in Nature, and without having recourse to the principle of indiscernibles it is quite clear that the germs of the same species do not all develop in the same uterus, at the same time, in the same place, in the same climate; in a word—in the same circumstances. Here are the causes of individual variation. The most efficacious single cause is the seminal liquor.
> (*8*, d, Part II, Chap. 8, Art. 338, p. 393)

Even in Bonnet's earliest writings on generation he had emphasised that the male contribution to sexual reproduction had considerable power to alter and control the subsequent development of the germ. Throughout all his works he continued to maintain that the male contributed no structure and that the semen was a mixture of inanimate matter which exerted its influence via nutrition (*8*, d, Part I,

Chap. 3, Art. 28, p. 101). At first he said nothing of the actual origin of the semen in the male. But in the second part of *Considérations* (first edition) he assumed that the molecules within the seminal liquor actually came from all parts of the male body, so that the fluid contained the juices or nutritive matter from all the father's organs, and was used to provide the nourishment for the corresponding parts of the germ (*8*, d, Part II, Chap. 8, Art. 338, pp. 394 ff.). This would account for the resemblances to the father. Thus Bonnet's theory had imposed upon preformation an additional hypothesis, confined at this stage to the male sex, which operated rather like the pangenic theories of heredity. It differed from Maupertuis' theory in that the molecules from the parent did not actually form the parts; but they did furnish a continuity between the generations and they modified, by nourishing them, the organs of the new generation. With this additional premise, Bonnet could explain almost all the facts, about monsters, hybrids and inheritance, which were then known to him.

Monsters with abortive or missing parts and those with extraordinary configurations in their organs were explained by assuming that the seminal liquor 'had been troubled or modified by some accident' (*8*, d, Part I, Chap. 3, Art. 34, p. 104). Those with a superabundance of parts must be the result of two germs developing together—a sort of modified Siamese twins—since no amount of alteration in the food would produce *additional structures*. Those whose 'parts were distributed in an abnormal way' (Bonnet accepted the usual classification of monsters, which had been common throughout the eighteenth century) presented most difficulty. At first Bonnet thought the germs must have been monstrous (*8*, d, Part I, Chap. 3, Art. 41, p. 104), but later he decided that these too might be the result of accidental alterations in the early nutrition of a perfect germ (*8*, d, Part II, Chap. 8, Art. 353, pp. 469 ff.).

Hybrids could be accommodated within the theory without much trouble. By this time it was clear that hybridisation was not an indiscriminate process, and that only fairly similar plants or animals could produce cross-breed offspring. Bonnet pointed out that this was exactly what one would predict from his theory. It was reasonable to suppose that the germ, within the female parent, could only be nourished by a seminal fluid very similar to that of the original species. If the liquid failed to stimulate the germ no offspring would result, but if the alien fluid did manage to initiate growth it would have a profound effect on the unfolding germ. The alterations would be mainly on the more inessential parts—the general form and distribution of the organs would remain like that of the maternal species which contributed the germ. Bonnet claimed that this had been confirmed by the observers, and it must be remembered that, when he first wrote, it was the Linnean school who had been interested in hybrids and that they, for different theoretical reasons, had emphasised just this point. But the best-known hybrid was still the mule, and while Bonnet found it easy on his theory to explain the elongated ears and slender tail, he was not too happy about the larynx (*8*, d, Part I, Chap. 3, Art. 41, pp. 109–11). This organ resembles that of the donkey and the animal brays. But it must, on Bonnet's view, be a modification of the larynx of the horse since the original germ came from a mare. Bonnet hopes further anatomical investigation may show this to be the case.

The first edition of the second part of *Les Considérations* contained a full account of the inheritance of polydactyly in the Kalleia family, as reported by Réaumur (*8*, d, Part II, Chap. 8, Art. 355, p. 478–306). It so happens that in this case, with one exception, the characteristic was transmitted by males. This Bonnet could explain on his theory of seminal nourishment; but Marie, a daughter who had inherited the characteristic from her father, married a normal male, and produced an affected son. On Bonnet's theory it was impossible for a woman to produce any change in the germs she guarded, so he tried to dismiss this case as due to other accidental causes. By the time Bonnet revised this work, he had discovered Maupertuis' account of the inheritance of polydactyly in the Ruhe family (see Chap. 6), and an additional report by a Dr Renou of similar cases in Bas-Anjou (*8*, d, Part II, footnote to Art. 355, p. 499). In the Ruhe family the six-fingered condition was, in several cases, passed on by the mother to the children, so that Bonnet could no longer think of Marie Kalleia as an exceptional case. He had, in fact, already suggested that, since the germ increases in size before fecundation, the mother must also contribute a nutritive juice. This was not a female seminal liquor, such as Maupertuis and others had postulated, but a food extracted from the female while the germ was still in the ovary. In the light of Maupertuis' observations on polydactyly this liquor now took on somewhat the same functions as the semen. So far as I know, Bonnet never actually gave it the same origin as he gave the semen, but he speaks of it acting on the germ 'in a manner more or less analogous to that of the semen'. In so far as he does so, the wheel has come full circle—the arch-preformationist has superimposed on his original theory a theory of biparental juices which, if it is not a pangenesis in the usual sense, is the complete logical equivalent. The parents do not pass on the characteristics but, by a system of pre-natal feeding, both of them modify the development of the perfect germ. This theory, Bonnet thought, would fully explain Maupertuis' results, and he noted triumphantly that the abnormality tended to disappear after repeated matings with five-fingered people—a fact which accorded perfectly with his ideas (*8*, d, Part II, Chap. 8, Art. 351).

But his reflections on the Ruhe family brought him face to face with another problem. He suddenly saw that unless he insisted on accidental causes he would be committed to such a stable world that no deviation or novelty could get started within it. So the first case of polydactyly must be due to accidental causes within one of the parents.

> If then the action of a certain semen on the germ can bring about the production or development of one or more supernumerary digits, why could there not be in the body of the women certain perturbatory causes which, acting on the germ in a manner more or less analogous to that of the semen of the six-fingered person, could produce more or less the same essential effect? Did the first six-fingered person who appeared in the world originate from fertilisation? If he did, whence came those hidden modifications in the organs of generation of his five-fingered father, upon which the six-fingeredness of the son depended? However that may be, the variations and irregularities of all kinds, such as are seen in six-fingeredness, indicate sufficiently well the intervention of purely accidental causes.
> (*8*, d, Part II, Chap. 8, footnote, p. 504)

All preformationists were opposed to Linneaus' idea that new species might arise as the result of hybridisation. Bonnet read with approval Adanson's *Mémoire* of 1769 (*33*, p. 154 ff.), and noted with satisfaction:

> M. Adanson, who is also concerned with this matter, made a number of experiments which seem to prove that there is, properly speaking, no transmutation of species amongst the vegetables, and that everything which is obtained by artificial fertilisation, using pollen from closely related species, can be reduced to more or less permanent varieties or to different sorts of monsters. But he always noted that the hybrid plants returned gradually to the maternal species.
> (*8*, d, Part II, Chap. 8, footnote, p. 517)

Adanson was a famous French botanist who investigated the peloric toadflax (Linnaeus), two species of Mercurialis (Merchant) and a deviant strawberry (Duchesne). All these sports had been reported during the eighteenth century and it was suggested that they were (a) hybrids and (b) new species. Adanson's experiments showed that these mutants did not breed true and he could find no evidence that they had a hybrid origin. He concluded that in all cases they were 'monsters', or as we would say 'mutants'.

Bonnet had heard of Koelreuter's work, but could not read German, so he had to rely on Haller's reports. In a letter to Bonnet, Haller wrote:

> The experiments on plants made by M. Koelreuter prove clearly that the germ is in the seed and that the male semen gives to the plants the growth and appearances of the father, without removing the innate predominance of the seed. These experiments are very interesting and carefully conducted.
> (*8*, d, Part II, Chap. 8, footnote, p. 317)

In the *Elementa Physiologiae* he stated:

> The accounts that we have of hybrids in animals are obscure; but what we know in this respect of plants is more certain. The structure of the mother plant is more apparent in the offspring because the hybrid plant retains the fecundity of the mother. It does not owe it to the male plant, and as a natural consequence plant hybrids revert to the maternal nature until they resemble it perfectly in structure.
> (*87*, Bk. 29, Vol. VIII, Sect. II, Art. 38, pp. 175–6)

These accounts seemed to accord so perfectly with Bonnet's view that he did not pursue the matter further. This is unfortunate, for had Bonnet been able to read the original, he would undoubtedly have given it the detailed consideration that he gave to the reports of Réaumur and Maupertuis. Had he done so, would it have caused him to alter his views? Possibly not; he could have explained most of Koelreuter's results in terms of the prolific seminal liquor, the maternal nutritive juice, and the stable germ. Certainly, he would have felt that many of his speculations had been confirmed. There was no transmutation of species by hybridisation—fertile hybrids do exist, but the progeny show variations and tend to revert to the parental forms. Hybrids can only be produced between very similar species, and pollen from the same species always fertilises or provokes growth more easily than does foreign pollen. These and many more facts commented on by Koelreuter would have been eagerly noted. It would have been interesting to see how he would have dealt with the identity of the range of varieties in reciprocal crosses. Would he have claimed that the supposed species were really varieties having identical germs? Or would he have held that, since the two species were very alike, the range of forms which could be produced by starting with germ 'A' and feeding it on a seminal fluid from 'B', would be almost identical to the range produced by starting with germ 'B' and feeding it with semen from 'A'? We shall never know but it is very easy to imagine him discussing the matter.

Even Charles Bonnet's greatest admirers must have felt a little overpowered by his final system. Few of his contemporaries can have been converted to it, but his views on many of the controversial issues were treated with respect and did exert more influence than we might expect. His ideas on preformation itself were accepted by many who might not have agreed with him on other points. Throughout the century the difficulties which attended preformation had been emphasised, and evidence against it had mounted. Yet the fundamental problem had remained—no adequate account had been offered of the formation of organised living things. Maupertuis' particles seemed inadequate for the task, and the empirical foundations of Buffon's and Needham's theories were doubtful. Yet the eighteenth century naturalists were unable to accept vitalism; nor were they content to confine themselves to merely descriptive biology. Bonnet's revised form of preformation appeared to provide an explanation for the newly discovered facts within the old framework. Moreover, although he had introduced many additional premises, these were of the desired physio-chemical nature, so that the theory, though more clumsy, was more mechanical. Hence, this revised version of preformation was accepted *faut de mieux* for the rest of the century.

II

Spallanzani

> '*The Volvox affords a new and beautiful instance of envelopment* (emboîtement), *the eye has been able to see the thirteenth generation; probably this is not the last. I cannot speak otherwise since nothing but time is wanting to investigate whether further development would appear.*'
>
> L. Spallanzani, TRACTS ON NATURAL HISTORY

SPALLANZANI, the third of the great preformationists of this period, added little to the theoretical aspects of the theory, but probably did more than Bonnet himself to bring about its acceptance. Spallanzani was undoubtedly one of the greatest experimental biologists of all time: his ingenuity in devising experiments, his technical skill in executing them, and his careful observation of his results, all combined to produce an outstanding investigator. He interested himself in a great many topics and made important discoveries in many aspects of biology—including the digestion, the circulation of the blood, and regeneration. Throughout his life he was particularly interested in generation, and it was in this connection that he performed some of his most famous experiments.

In 1765 and again in 1776 Spallanzani published accounts of series of experiments and microscopic observations which he had undertaken to test the ideas of Buffon and Needham (*71* and *72*). He repeated the latter's experiments with hot broth, but instead of corking the flasks, he used specially prepared vessels with long thin necks which could be fused by heat the moment the hot broth was placed in them. He then reheated the whole flask for almost an hour in a water bath, and after this treatment the infusions remained sterile for an indefinite period. When Needham protested that the heat had rendered the infusions themselves unsuitable for the maintenance of life, Spallanzani showed that, if the necks of the flasks were broken, the infusions very soon contained the usual swarm of living things. From these experiments, Spallanzani concluded that the objects seen within the infusions were living creatures whose germs had entered the liquid from the air, and were not vital particles produced by the breakdown of the fluid itself, as Buffon and Needham maintained. In connection with this work, Spallanzani conducted a series of investigations into the effects of heat, cold, and lack of air and liquid on the various animalculae found in different infusions, and also observed something more of their different forms and methods of propagation. He noted that some appeared to divide horizontally, others longitudinally; that some could bud or reproduce from pieces, while some, like volvox (*72*, Vol. I, Chap. 7, p. 142), burst to release the young which were contained within the cavity of the 'parent' body. Spallanzani noted this latter case as 'a new and beautiful instance of envelopment' (*72*, Vol. I, Chap. 7 and 8, pp. 118–74), This series of investigations refuted Needham, but they also advanced the study of the protozoa well beyond the point where Leeuwenhoek had left it.

At Bonnet's request, Spallanzani gave his attention to the seminal animals. First he examined the semen from a variety of animal species, including man as well as horse, dog, ram, carp, bull, newt and frog. His descriptions confirmed the observations of Leeuwenhoek and corrected the errors of Buffon. He had a poor opinion of the latter's ability as a microscopist and experimentalist. 'We descend', he says at one place, 'from the observations of Leeuwenhoek to those of Buffon' (*72*, Vol. I, Chap. 3, p. 320). Eventually, he decided that what Buffon had, in fact, observed were not the spermatozoa (seminal vermiculi) themselves, but various animalculae which had entered the semen (of dead men) from the air, and had developed in it as in an ordinary infusion (*72*, Vol. II, Chap. 4, pp. 1–18). Spallanzani concluded that the true spermatozoa were present in the semen before it left the testes, but that they did not live long in semen exposed to the air. He regarded the spermatozoa as genuine parasites whose habitat was the generative organs, and he believed that they were passed on from one generation to the next when the hosts copulated.

This view entailed that the seminal vermiculi must exist within the body of the young animal before the genital organs developed. Spallanzani suggested that they might exist, in a manner, in the blood, since

> I happened to observe in the mesenteric blood of a frog and three newts I know not how many of the seminal vermiculi peculiar to these amphibia. (*72*, Vol. II, Chap. 6, p. 61)

But he also noted

> I say, in a manner, because the rareness of the seminal vermiculi in the blood proves that it is not a fluid that agrees too well with them. (*72*, Vol. II, Chap. 6, p. 62)

Alternatively, since the semen must contact the eggs before fertilisation can take place, perhaps the parasites penetrated the new host at this time, and went straight to the developing generative organs, where they rested until the semen was produced. It is rather alarming to think that had Spallanzani really seen the penetration of the eggs by the spermatozoa he would have regarded it as a confirmation of this hypothesis. He presumed that the spermatozoa must propagate, but he noted that he had never seen them divide.

> Neither have I observed the vermiculi propagate by buds or shoots, like polypi. Therefore, abiding by the different modes of propagation hitherto known, it would appear a proper conclusion, that seminal vermiculi multiply by means of a foetus or eggs: but I must admit that neither the one nor the other has been seen by me. (*72*, Vol. II, Chap. 6, p. 64)

It was, of course, these observations and conclusions which helped to destroy Buffon's theory, but they also set the stage for Spallanzani's subsequent misinterpretation of his famous experiments on fertilisation.

Meanwhile Spallanzani had been investigating many other biological problems and, in the course of his work on the regeneration of animal parts, an account of which appeared in 1768 (*73*), he became a convert to ovism, just before he undertook the final investigation (at Bonnet's instigation) into the seminal vermiculi. He examined the regenerative powers of snails and of certain worms, and most especially of newts, frogs, salamanders and toads. (It was perhaps his use of amphibia in these investigations that prompted him to select them for the bulk of his work on sexual reproduction.) In his study of regeneration in tadpoles he traced their life history backwards, and was led on to investigate the development of the eggs themselves. In his account of his investigation he produced the following argument for ovism:

It appears therefore plainly that the tadpoles exist before fecundation, which most interesting truth may, for the sake of precision, be thus demonstrated. The unfecundated eggs do not differ in the least from those that are fecundated; these last are nothing else but the tadpoles themselves coiled up and concentrated: the same is therefore equally true of the unfertilised egg: and consequently the tadpoles exist before fecundation and require only the fecundating liquid of the male to unfold themselves.
(*71*, Vol. I, Chap. 1, Sect. XIX, p. 18)

An almost identical argument appeared at the beginning of his final work on this subject, *Expérience sur la Génération*, which was published in 1785 (*71*, Vol. III, Introduction, Section XV, p. 14). Spallanzani started these later investigations by establishing that, contrary to general opinion, the eggs of the amphibia were fertilised outside the body of the female. He not only observed the coupling of frogs and toads, but also proved the matter experimentally by killing the females as the eggs were being emitted. Those eggs which were removed from the interior of the animal failed to develop but those which had been shed and had, therefore, been in contact with the semen from the males, grew into tadpoles in the normal way. In order to confirm this result, Spallanzani made little taffeta pants for the male animals, which enabled them to mount and couple with the females, but prevented the semen they ejected from reaching the eggs. None of the eggs produced under these conditions developed, but if some of these eggs were then selected and touched with the semen they grew into tadpoles.

Spallanzani had always believed that the semen must come into contact with the eggs before fertilisation could occur, but many physiologists still maintained that this was unnecessary, and that a vapour, the *aura seminalis* given off by the semen, could effect fertilisation. In order to test this hypothesis, Spallanzani placed a small open vessel containing semen within another vessel to the sides of which the gelatinous eggs adhered. The whole was then sealed and kept warm so that the eggs were bathed in the vapour from the evaporating semen. The result was always negative, and no matter how near Spallanzani brought the eggs to the semen—providing that there was no actual contact between the two—the eggs always failed to develop. A sample of these eggs was subsequently touched by the semen in the vessel and these eggs developed normally.

Spallanzani had already fertilised frogs' eggs artificially, but he now decided to try the same kind of experiment with other animals. He was successful in the case of toads, silk moths and finally with a bitch of the spaniel type (Barbet). Of this latter experiment he wrote:

> The success of this experiment gave me more pleasure than I have ever felt in any of my other scientific researches.
> (*71*, Vol. III, Chap. 5, Section CLXXIII, p. 226)

Bonnet immediately suggested that he should now try to produce hybrids by inseminating the bitch with semen from other animals. But, instead, Spallanzani extended his work to the plant kingdom, and repeated the experiments of Camerarius and others on dioecious plants such as spinach, dog's mercury and the like. He was, of course, convinced that the plant embryo must exist in the ovules before fertilisation, but his results seemed to prove that pollen was not always necessary for the production of seed. Perhaps Spallanzani overlooked the occasional heterosexual flower that can appear in such plants but, whatever the cause of his error, this series of experiments threw doubt on the true sexuality of plants, and gave rise to the suggestion that parthenogenesis was widespread in the plant kingdom.

Spallanzani believed that, in animals, the semen promoted growth because it stimulated the foetal heart. If this were the case then there was no reason why other substances might not be substituted for it. With his characteristic thoroughness, Spallanzani tried to fertilise frogs' eggs with a great number of different things, starting with blood from the adult heart and juices extracted from the heart itself, and passing on to try the effect of electricity (which was said to speed up the growth of fertilised eggs, but to have no effect on non-fertilised specimens) and numerous chemical stimulants. He tried vinegar and spirits of wine diluted in water and urine, which merely made the eggs decay more quickly instead of fertilising them. The juices of lemons and limes, and the oil from their skins, was equally powerless to bring about fertilisation (*71*, Vol. III, Sections CLXVIII–CLXII, pp. 213–18). Only the juices from the testicles themselves had the same effect as the semen.

While no substitute could be found for the semen, a very little semen was surprisingly effective, and was even more effective if diluted with a little water. Spallanzani started to enquire into the limits of this dilution. To his surprise he discovered that:

. . . three grains of semen mixed with twelve or eighteen ozs of water will communicate to the mixture its prolific virtue, in such a way that the eggs placed in it will develop into tadpoles. Meanwhile these three grains of semen have spread into the entire mass of water, but how rare has it become in spreading out thus, how few of the spermatic particules will touch the eggs? There are other facts which prove the prolific virtue of semen even in the tiniest of quantities. Thus I have proved that a drop of water 1/50 of a line in diameter, taken from eighteen ozs of water in which three grains of semen had been mixed, can still fertilise the eggs. I wished to see the proportion between the volume of the egg to be fertilised, which in the frog is a sphere 4/5 of a line in diameter, and the volume of the spermatic particles contained in a water drop 1/50 of a line in diameter, and I found the volume of the egg was to the volume of the spermatic particles in the drop of water as 1,064,777,777 to 1. . . . This result led me to seek another—what was the weight of the spermatic particles spread throughout the water drop? I found that it was 1/2,994,687,500 of a grain: finally I wanted to know the exact volume of the spermatic particles. . . . I found it was approximately 1/3,084,120,420 of a cubic line.
(*71*, Vol. III, Chap. 4, Art. 155, pp. 190–1)

(Spallanzani, as an ovist, made no distinction between the unfertilised eggs and the tadpoles, calling them by the same name. To prevent confusion, I translated the word 'Totard' as 'egg' where appropriate.)

Spallanzani had discovered that the semen was a very powerful substance which could act in minute quantities, but he firmly believed that its action was mechanical or chemical, and he compared its potency to that of snake venom and storax. His last set of experiments was designed to obtain additional information concerning the nature of the semen itself. Using a mixture of semen and water, he applied a series of physical and chemical tests. He found that its potency could be reduced by evacuating the surrounding air, or by slow evaporation. Complete desiccation destroyed its potency entirely, as did very violent agitation, exposure to the fumes of candles, paper or tobacco, or the addition of such substances as common salt, vinegar, spirits of wine, or oil. Though mild heat did not affect it, heat above 30°C diminished its power, which was completely destroyed if the temperature was raised above 35° or 40°C. Similarly, long exposure to very low temperatures reduced its power and eventually rendered it useless. Spallanzani should surely have seen that the semen behaved much like a living thing and was responding in a way that was very reminiscent of the animalcules. But if he did, he did not mention the fact. Indeed, he makes almost no comment on the results of these tests (*71*, Vol. III, pp. 298–310).

His last test is the most famous. In this he tried the effect of filtering the mixture of semen and water. If it was passed through cotton, chiffon or any other material, the liquid lost some of its power to fertilise the eggs, and if it was passed through one or two filter papers the power was reduced in the same way. The loss was greater if another paper was added, and the liquid was completely useless if it was passed through six or seven papers. On the other hand, if the sediment left on the filter papers was redissolved immediately in pure water, the new mixture was as potent as ever.

Spallanzani's enquiries on generation reached a new level in experimental biology and many of his results have stood the test of time. That they did almost nothing to clarify the basic issues, and that the results were misinterpreted by both Spallanzani and his contemporaries, was of course largely due to the current belief in the preformation theory. It was this theory, on the other hand, which inspired those investigations, and many of the experiments were the direct result of Spallanzani's beliefs. And even if, *per impossibile*, Spallanzani had been able to conduct his experiments without any theoretical background, it is doubtful whether, in the absence of the cell theory, they could have been correctly interpreted. The techniques which Spallanzani devised and the facts he discovered remained as a basis on which, once the general outlook had changed, others could build.

12

The Investigations of Prévost and Dumas, 1821–7

'*This conviction [that biological activity is susceptible to a chemical and physical explanation] has given us confidence in our work, and gives us grounds to hope that it will not be impossible to discover, by means of careful experimentation, the natural laws which jointly produce the vital activities. Convinced that there is nothing miraculous in them, we are resolved to study all aspects and we seek to join our observations with those of the physiologists who preceded us.*'

Introduction to Prévost's and Dumas' First Paper,
ANNALES DES SCIENCES NATURELLES, 1824

THE late eighteenth century version of the preformation theory must have been known to a relatively large public. The interests of its proponents and the type of works they produced were sufficient to ensure this result. Haller had incorporated his views in the *Elementa Physiologiae*, which was used as a medical textbook. Even the abridged version of this eight-volume work contained a brief account of his views on generation, so it is unlikely that any doctor trained at a university in France, Britain, Switzerland, or even Germany, between 1770 and 1820, would have been ignorant of the theory. Bonnet's vast philosophical system was based entirely on his belief in preformation and again his works, of which there were a fair number of editions, were read by a wide but very different type of public. The results of Spallanzani's investigations were always published in Italian but many were immediately translated into English and French, so that they too must have had a fair circulation amongst the naturalists of all three countries. In spite of this widespread knowledge of their views, the ideas of these preformationists seem to have received relatively little discussion. Nor did they provoke a great number of new investigations.

There are, I think, two different reasons for this reaction. In the first place, the results of over a hundred years of research and interest had convinced the late eighteenth century naturalists that generation was an extremely difficult subject. Haller, himself, introduced the section 'On the Foetus' in the *Elementa Physiologiae* with the remark:

> I now start on a most difficult enquiry and can scarcely promise any conclusion which will satisfy the reader.
> (*87*, Bk. 29, Part I, Art. 1, p. 1)

Cruikshank (*13*, p. 197), who saw the very young embryo of the rabbit in the fallopian tubes and who almost discovered the mammalian egg, and Haighton (*36*, p. 159), who investigated the nature of fertilisation, both apologised for returning to a subject where so little progress seemed possible. Their papers appeared before the Royal Society in 1797, and by that time the belief that generation was so difficult that it was useless to study it seemed to be fairly widespread.

The second reason why there was so little direct follow-up of the eighteenth century work is connected with a general change in the scientific life in Europe. In the previous period the republic of learning had constituted a fairly homogeneous group of people, whose general standards were fairly similar and amongst whom there were no real national distinctions. News of new results passed readily from one country to another amongst the small group of scientists who shared similar aims and whose assessments of the importance of any investigation were much the same. But gradually the situation had changed. By the beginning of the nineteenth century this unity was lost, and within biology there were distinct differences both in approach and in the subjects studied, between Germany, England and France. The change was probably due to a variety of causes. New topics were being pursued, and these tended to attract attention primarily in those countries where there was a stimulating pioneer or where conditions were in other ways particularly favourable. Some aspects of biology had now advanced to a stage where training, equipment and laboratory facilities were necessary, and this in turn meant that in general they could only be pursued in universities or institutions, whose availability varied in the different countries.

In Germany there was a great increase in the interest shown in biology between 1790 and 1830 but the work continued in relative isolation. The reorientation of outlook brought about by the romantic movement and the subsequent development of nature philosophy were responsible for this interest. The results of this intellectual revolution, which will be discussed in the next chapter, eventually spread well beyond Germany, but they were naturally more strongly felt within Germany itself. The approach of these workers was so different that in many cases their writings could not be understood by anyone who did not understand their presuppositions.

In Britain all biological progress was in the hands of amateurs—the universities neither taught biology nor encouraged research. Sir Joseph Banks, for example, had to find and maintain a private tutor to teach him botany while he was at Oxford (*5*, p. 6). Hence the biologists had no formal training and practically no facilities. Very little experimental work of a complicated nature could be done, and the main preoccupation was with systematics, which was stimulated by the appearance of new specimens of the flora and fauna of the Pacific and Australasia. The only work which had any bearing on generation was that done by the breeders, but even here the workers were mainly concerned with the practical implications. Andrew Knight published his first paper on the subject in 1799 (*42*, p. 195), and later sent to the Horticultural Society accounts of the crosses of various fruit trees. At about the same time Herbert (*37*) was also experimenting on the crossing of various garden plants, and Goss and Seton (*34*) were investigating the effects of cross-pollination between various varieties of garden peas. In the latter experiments Goss noted (a) that the hybrids of a blue and white seed cross were all white, and (b) that these seeds produced plants bearing all blue, all white or a mixture of blue and white seeds.

In France there was more continuity between the eighteenth and nineteenth century work in biology. This is not surprising, since the great biologists of the eighteenth century had been either French or had been intellectually centred on France. Moreover, after the revolution there was some Government support for science, so that it was possible for a few scientists to work at institutions or at universities. Although some biologists, such as Lamarck and Geoffroy St Hilaire, were influenced by the new Romantic outlook, the majority continued to preserve and develop the attitudes of the previous period. On the whole there was at this time a welcome reaction against speculative theories, and a great increase in the emphasis on experiment and observation. The only work on generation which followed the lines of the main eighteenth century investigations was done in France, or in places influenced by the intellectual life of France.

The most important investigations of this type were those conducted by Prévost and Dumas, who continued the work on generation along the lines laid down by Spallanzani. Their first paper on the subject was published in Geneva in 1821, but their main contributions appeared in the newly founded *Annales des Sciences Naturelles* between 1824 and 1827 (*26* and *27*). In its entirety, their work constituted the most complete and systematic review of the subject up to this time, and it is surprising that it has not received more attention from historians.

The first series of three papers which appeared in 1824 (*27*, Vol. 1, pp. 1, 167 and 294) were concerned exclusively with the male contribution to generation. Having given a brief survey of the various types of male generative organs in the animal kingdom, they pointed to the common presence of the testes in both vertebrates and invertebrates, and concluded that these organs must be regarded as the source of the essential secretion. Obviously influenced by the current emphasis on the comparative method, Prévost and Dumas set out to examine the secretion in as many animals as possible. The number they observed was extremely large and included representatives of many classes of mammals, birds, amphibia, fishes and even some invertebrates. They discovered that in all cases the semen contained motile elements and that these were present in both the juices extracted from the testes and in the semen after ejaculation. They concluded that the spermatozoa were therefore the essential part of the secretion and that they must be formed within the testes by some process which they did not understand. Moreover, they reconfirmed the fact that semen from very young and immature animals lacked these motile parts, as did the semen of the infertile mules and hinnies. Using the semen of the dog as a standard, they compared the size and the number of the different spermatozoa and gave some description of the different forms. They used an uncorrected compound miscroscope and in one place they remarked:

> These observations could not have been carried out without the excellent microscope of M. Amici.
> (*27*, a, Vol. I, p. 281)

In fact this miscroscope was probably still very poor, for the drawings show less accurate detail than many eighteenth century efforts. They are, in fact, less informative than some produced by Leeuwenhoek. However, in general, Prévost's and Dumas' results confirmed the observations of Leeuwenhoek and Spallanzani. Like the latter they emphasised that the spermatozoa were unlike the infusoria in behaviour, origin and form, and they therefore regarded Buffon's suggestion that spermatozoa resulted from decomposition of the semen as being completely without foundation. They revived, for the first time in a hundred years, the suggestion that the spermatozoa were the essential male contribution to generation.

The second monograph by Prévost and Dumas appeared in the second volume of the *Annales des Sciences Naturelles* (27, Vol. II, pp. 100 and 129) and in it they reported on the investigations into fertilisation itself. Using frogs, they repeated and amplified Spallanzani's work on the subject without drawing his erroneous conclusions. Taking a batch of eggs they divided them into two parts: one half they placed in distilled water and the other in distilled water containing the juice extracted from the testes. They noted that the eggs in distilled water increased in size due to the absorption of water, and that if blood were added to the water the red colour was also absorbed. After about four hours the eggs ceased to increase, and remained unchanged until about the second day when they started to decompose. The eggs to which semen had been added also absorbed water, but after a few hours they started to undergo further changes. Prévost and Dumas described with precision the early stages of development including the initial cleavage without, of course, being able to interpret them in terms of the cell theory. In order to show that a material contact between the egg and the semen was essential to fertilisation they devised an improved version of Spallanzani's vapour chamber but, of course, none of the eggs exposed to the fumes from semen did, in fact, develop.

Their next series of experiments was designed to demonstrate that it was the spermatozoa themselves which were responsible for fertilisation. They showed that after complete desiccation the semen contained no motile spermatozoa, and that the solid residue, redissolved in distilled water, was unable to fertilise fresh eggs. An electrical current had a similar effect—it both killed the spermatozoa and rendered the semen useless. If semen mixed with distilled water was passed through filter papers, some of the spermatozoa were retained on the filter papers and the filtrate was correspondingly less potent. When five filter papers were employed, the filtrate was seen to be completely devoid of spermatozoa and was also incapable of fertilising any eggs. The residue to which distilled water was again added contained motile spermatozoa and could be used to fertilise eggs. There was therefore a complete correlation between the presence of spermatozoa and fertility in the semen.

Prévost and Dumas believed that each spermatozoon acted individually on one egg, and they thought that they had once seen one spermatozoon penetrating the gelatinous envelope of the egg. It is difficult to demonstrate this correlation experimentally, but two sets of experiments gave some support to the idea. In one set samples, each containing five grammes of semen, were mixed with various known quantities of distilled water and added to a known number of eggs. The number of fertilisations was recorded. It had already been noted that semen was more efficient if it was mixed with water and that it became less efficient if deprived of liquid. The addition of its own weight of water and of double the weight increased the efficiency of the semen, but subsequent additions made no difference, nor did the presence of more eggs. That amount of semen was capable of fertilising between twelve and seventeen eggs and this remained fairly constant. In the next set of experiments Prévost and Dumas released a known number of spermatozoa upon a known and greater number of eggs. In all cases the number of eggs which developed were less than the number of spermatozoa employed—a result which was in perfect accord with the idea that each egg was fertilised by a single spermatozoon although, of course, it did not prove the hypothesis.

Having studied fertilisation in frogs, Prévost and Dumas turned their attention to the more difficult subject of fertilisation in mammals. Their monograph on this subject was also published in the *Annales des Sciences Naturelles* (27, *b*, pp. 100 and 129). Using dogs and rabbits, they examined the ovaries before and after copulation. They redescribed the changes in the Graafian follicles and the ultimate formation of the corpus luteum. Some days after copulation, they discovered small ovoid bodies in the lower part of the oviducts and in the horns of the uterus, which they identified as the precursors of the embryos. This reconfirmed Cruikshank's discoveries, and completely disproved Buffon's contention that the contents of the Graafian follicles passed down the oviducts in a liquid form. These small 'developing ovules' (the blastulas) were only about one or two millimetres in diameter, whereas the Graafian follicles were about seven or eight millimetres across. Hence, Prévost and Dumas pointed out, the bodies discovered by de Graaf (commonly known as the Graafian ova) could not themselves be the eggs, but must produce much smaller objects. They were not the first to make this suggestion—indeed de Graaf himself had hinted at it and Haller had made a somewhat similar suggestion though he did not back his ideas with such a detailed collection of facts—but they were amongst the first to insist that the terminology should be changed to make the matter clear:

> We would like to give the name *vesicle* to the bodies found in the ovaries as this better reflects their nature.
> (*27*, b, pp. 135–6)

They never claimed to have identified the eggs in the follicles, nor to have seen the first stages in the development of the mammalian foetus. But they really came very near to making this important discovery for they described a body, about one millimetre in diameter, which was visible under the surface of the ripe follicle just before it ruptured, which was obviouslyt he ovum on the discus proligerus. They also pointed out that no spermatozoa were visible near the ovary in mammals and that eggs in the ovaries of frogs could not be fertilised, from which they concluded that the true eggs in mammals were probably fertilised within the oviducts. Prévost's and Dumas' three monographs had established few new facts but they had consolidated the previous discoveries and reduced to order a welter of conflicting claims which had obscured the truth. Their work constituted a genuine and successful attempt to put the facts about generation on a firm basis of observation and experiment.

The attitude of Prévost and Dumas to theoretical problems is of considerable interest to an historian trying to get a true picture of this period in the history of ideas on generation. Little influenced by the current change in the metaphysical outlook, these workers represent the continuity between the eighteenth and nineteenth centuries. In the introduction to their first paper they make a point of stressing their mechanistic approach to biology:

> It is however quite evident that there occur in animals two sorts of

phenomena which it is impossible to confuse with each other. There are intellectual phenomena, whose manifestation presupposes an immaterial principle, concerning whose particular nature it is impossible to frame any precise ideas. There are bodily phenomena which seem to be susceptible of a purely physical explanation, since we see in them only an elaboration of already existing material without any creation, and since in many cases, when the action is of a simple enough nature, it is easy to demonstrate the series of chemical and physical effects which determine the result. This conviction has given us some confidence in our work, and gives us grounds to hope that it will not be impossible to discover, by means of careful experimentation, the natural laws which jointly produce the vital activities. Convinced that there is nothing miraculous in them, we are resolved to study all aspects and we seek to join our observations with those of the physiologists who preceded us.
(*27*, a, Vol. I, p. 3)

Having such an outlook, it is to be expected that Prévost and Dumas will have no metaphysical reasons for rejecting theories which give a causal explanation of generation, and that they will in fact hope to find a satisfactory theory of this type. Their comments on the views of their predecessors confirm this expectation.

They noted that:

Epigenesis, which had been abandoned, is, to some extent, returning to favour; but this vague explanation accommodates itself so easily to the particular opinions and wishes of each of the learned men who adopt it, that one very seldom finds two of them who are in agreement on the principal facts.
(*27*, a, Vol. I, p. 6–7)

They discussed the preformation theory in greater detail and they allowed that:

At first sight this hypothesis is startling, but gradually the mind gets used to it and soon comes to prefer it to any other. It seems easier to imagine a time when nature, as it were, laboured and gave birth all at once to the whole of creation, present and future, than to imagine a continual activity. . . .
(*27*, a, Vol. I, p. 5)

The most recent and complete version of the theory, that of Charles Bonnet, naturally received the most attention—they wrote of it:

> Although these simple principles startle our imagination, they make good enough sense of the phenomena, and certainly their author was too well versed in the science of analysis to admit them if he had not found them in agreement with the known conditions of the problem. . . .
> (*27*, a, Vol. I, p. 6)

Nevertheless Prévost and Dumas were convinced that the theory must be rejected because

> His [Bonnet's] fundamental idea remains without proof and becomes therefore a gratuitous hypothesis of historical interest only.

Their criticism was completely justified, for by the time Bonnet had altered his theoretical assumptions to accommodate all the evidence, the preformation of the germs had become removed from all verification or refutation.

Their attitude to this theory reflects a definite trend which appeared in many scientists of this period. Tired of the facile speculations of the previous era, they were in reaction against all rationalistic hypotheses. It was not sufficient that the assumptions of a theory should make good sense of the phenomena—they must do so by assuming 'true causes', i.e. they must postulate processes or states of affairs of which we have some independent knowledge. This criterion for a good theory was to have profound effects in some other branches of science, e.g. geology, but it could not be used successfully in the study of generation. In addition to this new rigour on the theoretical side, there was an increased emphasis, amongst this group of scientists, on the importance of experimentation. Chemistry had made enormous advances in the preceding period, and it was generally conceded that this success was also a triumph for the experimental approach. Dumas, himself a chemist, made this point to support his plea for an experimental approach to the subject of generation (*27*, a, Vol. I, p. 11).

In spite of their admirable views on methodology and in spite of their careful experiments and observations, Prévost and Dumas ultimately produced theories which were little better than those they criticised. In 1825 and 1826 they continued to publish the results of various investigations into the development of different animals (*27*, c, pp. 47 and 49 and d, p. 447), and in 1827 Dumas published his final theory (*27*, e, p. 443). In this last work, Dumas suggested that the spermatozoon, having penetrated into the egg, forms the primitive streak and later gives rise to the nervous system; all the other organs are formed from the egg itself. There is thus a continuity between the generations, and both parents contribute to the offspring. Dumas claimed that such a theory would account for the preservation of type between the generations, and also for the resemblance of the offspring to both or either parent. In addition it provided an explanation for the gradual development of the embryo, without assuming the old theory of *emboîtement*, for which there was no evidence.

Prévost held a slightly different view, which was stated in a letter published along with Dumas' article. Like Dumas, he believed the spermatozoon reached the cicatricula of a fowl's egg and formed the median axis, but he thought that the foetus, which developed gradually as a result of this stimulation, contained nothing of either the ovum or the spermatozoon. Thus Prévost's theory was one of pure epigenesis, whereas Dumas' was a modification of the original preformation doctrine.

Dumas' theory was not original—some Greeks had suggested a somewhat similar view (although they had thought in terms of distinct organs) and the idea had been revived in 1825 by Rolando (*67*). Its reappearance at this time is interesting, for it reflects a change in the ideas on the organisation of living things. Anyone attempting to give a causal account of the development of a new organism must assume that the elements from which it develops are not completely structureless, but contain some fundamental units which can initiate the differentiation of the new organism. What sort of unit is envisaged depends on the prevailing views of the nature of vital organisation. The seventeenth and eighteenth century form of preformation was dictated by the belief that an organism was a unity built up from organs. Towards the end of the eighteenth century new ideas on vital organisation began to appear. Haller drew attention to the reappearance in different organs of certain types of material having definite textures. Bichat investigated these textures (tissues) more thoroughly, and suggested that it was these rather than the organs which should be regarded as the fundamental units of life:

> All animals are an assemblage of different organs, which, executing each a function, concur in their own manner, to the preservation of the whole. It is several separate machines in a general one that constitutes the individual. Now these separate machines are themselves formed by many textures of a very different nature, and which really compose the elements of these

organs. Chemistry has its simple bodies, which form, by the combinations of which they are susceptible, the compound bodies, such as caloric, light, hydrogen, oxygen, carbon, azote, phosphorus, etc. In the same way anatomy has its simple elements which, by their combinations four with four, six with six, eight with eight, etc. make the organs. . . .

These are the true organised elements of our bodies. Their nature is con-constantly the same, wherever they are met with. As in chemistry, the simple bodies do not alter, notwithstanding the different compound ones they form. . . .

Much has been said since the time of Bordeu, of the peculiar life of each organ, which is nothing else than that particular character which distinguishes the combination of the vital properties of one organ, from those of another. Before these properties had been analysed with exactness and precision, it was clearly impossible to form a correct idea of this peculiar life. From the account I have just given of it, it is evident that the greatest part of the organs being comprised of very different simple textures, the idea of a peculiar life can only apply to these simple textures, and not to the organs themselves.
(*6* and *37*, pp. 69 and 71)

It was because they accepted these ideas that men like Rolando, Prévost and Dumas could escape from the *emboîtement* theory. Since they viewed living things as an assemblage of different fundamental tissues, they were no longer so deeply puzzled by the appearances and existence of nervous or blood tissue before the animal had acquired the full complement of organs. It was also easier to think of these elements separately, and therefore easier to suppose that one sex might donate the rudiments of one tissue and the opposite sex the rudiments of another.

The investigations of Prévost and Dumas attracted relatively little attention. Perhaps neither scientist felt that their results had led to any definite conclusions, for, after 1827, both abandoned the subject and never returned to it. Yet their discoveries have stood the test of time: the Graafian follicle does emit an ovum, the ovum and the spermatozoon do meet in the fallopian tube, the spermatozoa are the essential male elements and only one spermatozoon is required to fertilise an ovum. The main difficulty about these results was that, even if the tissues were accepted as the basic vital units, they still could not be understood. Once the cell theory was formulated these facts had a new significance—without the cell theory nothing could be made of them.

13

The Influence of the Nature Philosophers and von Baer's Embryological Work

'It is quite certain that we cannot become sufficiently acquainted with organised creatures and their hidden potentialities by aid of purely mechanical natural principles, much less can we explain them; and this is so certain, that we very boldy assert that it is absurd for man even to conceive such an idea, and to hope that a Newton may one day arise even to make the production of a blade of grass comprehensible, according to natural laws ordained by no intentions, such an insight we must absolutely deny to man.'

Kant, CRITIQUE OF JUDGEMENT

TOWARDS the end of the eighteenth century the intellectual climate of Europe underwent a spectacular change. Romanticism replaced the mechanistic outlook of the previous period. The exact nature and origin of the new ideas has been a matter of considerable research. Professor Lovejoy (*48*, pp. 207–28), in particular, has shown how misleading it is to classify such a diversity of opinions under one name. Nevertheless, there was a considerable change, which one authority has summed up as follows:

> Towards the close of the century there developed in Europe a number of tendencies representing in part a reaction against the ideas of the Newtonian world, in part a recrudescence of the forces that had remained present in western civilisation since the Renaissance. These tendencies, loosely grouped together as romanticism, emphasised the emotional rather than the rational side of human nature, a richly diversified development of individuals rather than a mathematical uniformity and, most significant of all, the genesis and growth of things rather than their mechanical ordering. (*63*, p. 395)

The Romantics themselves might have had little effect on biology, since their main interests were in literature, art and politics. But the philosophers of the period, especially in Germany, gradually produced a series of metaphysical systems which incorporated and systematised much of the romantic approach. These philosophers differed amongst themselves but, like the artists whose views they reflected, they were chiefly interested in human affairs—in religion, morals and politics. In spite of this, their ideas had a profound effect on all sciences throughout the early part of the nineteenth century.

If an investigation into a subject has produced a theory which fits the facts and gives rise to testable predictions which have, so far, been confirmed—and which is, for the time being, completely satisfactory—then that subject will be relatively insensitive to changes in the intellectual climate. If not, it will naturally be more open to such influences. Thus, although many romantic philosophers disapproved of Newtonian mechanics this science remained relatively unchanged by the new views. Their views had little effect on the better established scientific theories, but the less well developed branches of both physics and chemistry were considerably altered. It was, however, in biology that the changes were the most profound and far-reaching. This was partly because no branch of biology had as yet achieved a truly scientific theory (in the above sense) but it was also because the whole outlook of philosophers such as Herder, Fichte, Schelling and Hegel had more direct implications for biology than for any other science. In general, these philosophers saw the Universe, not as a machine produced by a Creator, who then remained a spectator, but rather as a living whole in which the Spirit or Will was constantly present. The observed phenomena were seen as nothing but manifestations of this Will, and all attempts to reduce these diversities to mere matter and motion were regarded as absurd. Kant, who was much more impressed with Newtonian science than most of his German contemporaries, believed that mechanical principles could be of some use in the understanding of living things. But, as the quotation at the beginning of this chapter shows, he was quite definite that living things could never be fully explained by them.

The biologists who took these philosophical views seriously were, of course, vitalists. Many of them regarded it as axiomatic that the phenomena they observed could not be explained by any underlying causal physico-chemical processes. Instead they looked for explanation of a radically different kind, which had much in common with the Aristotelian idea of a formal cause. Nature could only be understood by studying the diversities of its forms, but these forms were all variations of a limited number of ideal types or archetypes which, like the Platonic idea, were never fully realised in the actual organisms. Thus all animals were seen as variations of about four or five such archetypes. Animals within any group were all regarded as more or less modified versions of the one plan. In a similar manner the higher plants were reduced to a single basic plan of leaves, stem, and roots—Goethe's attempt to show that all the floral parts were modified leaves was an early example of this approach. This new outlook meant that comparative anatomy and morphology were popular subjects and, from the time of Goethe, knowledge of these branches of biology increased at a great pace. Indeed, much of the information which was later used by the evolutionists was collected by men who approached comparative morphology in this way.

These philosophers also emphasised that no individual or institution could be understood without a knowledge of its gradual development, and this meant that there was a great interest in the history of everything—beliefs, customs, traditions, races and people. This affected the biologists in two distinct ways. In the first place they became interested in the history of living things. At the time that these ideas first became influential, the 'Great Chain of Being' was widely accepted, but an increased knowledge of fossils and of geological facts caused many to reinterpret the idea. They now assumed that there was no single act of creation, which produced all links of the Chain at once, but rather that the higher organisms had gradually developed from the simpler kinds in a unilateral evolution. Others denied that one creature had evolved from another, but believed that they had appeared successively, each new and more complicated kind being a fresh manifestation of God's will. Oken apparently subscribed to this latter view for, in *Lehrbuch der Naturphilosophie* in 1810, he stated that:

> The philosophy of Nature is the science of the eternal transformation of God into the world

and

> It has the task of showing the phases of the world's evolution from primal nothingness: how the heavenly bodies and elements arose, how these

> advanced to higher forms, how finally organisms appeared and in man attained to reason. These phases constitute the history of the generation of the universe. . . . The philosophy of nature is in the most comprehensive sense cosmogony or, as Moses called it, Genesis.
> (*49*, Lecture XI, p. 320)

Thus whether they believed in an actual evolution or in a sort of gradual manifestation of complexity, many biologists now believed that living things had a history, and that the kinds of plants and animals which exist now differ from those which existed in other times.

In the second place, this general interest in history meant that biologists paid more attention to individual developments since this was the history of the organism itself. A large number of biologists, including Serres, Oken, Kieser, Meckel, Pander, Dollinger, Remak, Berlin, Koelliker and von Baer, wrote works on embryology. Some, like Oken, were extremely interested in the current philosophy, and their scientific writings were distinctly speculative. Others, like von Baer, were not much interested in the actual philosophical systems, but were still influenced by the opinions of the times and accepted the above presuppositions. As far as von Baer himself was concerned, his interest in and knowledge of the contemporary philosophers has been discussed at some length by A. W. Meyer (see *53*, pp. 59–66).

As we have seen, the eighteenth century attempts at a causal account of generation failed, and preoccupation with the question gave rise to a welter of speculative theories. Scientists working within the new metaphysical framework were freed from this problem. Growth accompanied by change was now regarded as a fundamental feature of the Universe, and the growth of living things was the analogy in terms of which all other processes were to be understood. It, therefore, seemed a basic phenomenon requiring no further explanation. What had been an atypical, almost miraculous process from the seventeenth and eighteenth century point of view, became the paradigm of the natural for the nature philosophers.

The scientists were therefore free to observe and describe; so there was, with some few exceptions, a significant increase in the empirical content of embryological works. True to their theoretical principles, they set out to look for general descriptive or phenomenological laws. A great deal of attention was paid to the comparative development of the different organs and systems, and to the changes of form which each embryo underwent. At first it was suggested that each animal, as it developed, assumed, in ascending scale, the forms of all the lower types. A. Étienne-Renaud Augustine Serres is usually supposed to be the originator of this suggestion. Thus man, on this view, would be first a worm, then a simple vertebrate, then a fish, a reptile and a lower mammal, before the human form was achieved. This idea gained considerable currency: von Baer, writing in 1828, referred to it as 'the generally accepted conception'. It was clearly closely connected with the idea of the 'Great Chain of Being', a point which von Baer also acknowledged, although he seemed to believe that the law of development gave rise to the idea of the Chain of Being:

> Hence it was that I asserted above, that the view of the unilateral progression of animals was necessarily connected with the prevailing idea as to the law of development.
> (*86*, and *37*, pp. 392 ff.)

For those biologists who saw the Chain of Being as the result of an evolutionary process, this law suggested, for the first time, that 'ontogeny reflects phylogeny'. However it must be noted that it would be quite possible to accept the Chain of Being in a static sense, and still to hold this law of development. Moreover, even if it were accepted that this embryological law held because it reflected the course of evolution, both the law and the accepted phylogeny were very different from those which Haeckel suggested later in the century.

Von Baer's work on embryology, which was published in 1828, showed what an enormous increase in detailed knowledge had taken place in the first thirty years of the nineteenth century. In part this was due to von Baer himself, but the second part of the book, which is really a very complete survey of the comparative development of many different groups, does include the information which has been collected by his immediate predecessors. As a result of this new knowledge of comparative embryology, von Baer suggested an entirely new law of development. Like the law described above, which von Baer set out to refute, it was a phenomenological law and made no reference to any causal processes. In the conclusion of his work, von Baer summed it up in the following general way:

> The history of the development of the individual is the history of its increasing individuality in all respects.
> (*37*, p. 399)

While, in this general form, the law accorded perfectly with the prevailing view on growth and development, which emphasised just this aspect, it was also an almost self-evident truth. Both these points seem to have struck von Baer, for he added:

> This general result is indeed so simple, that it would seem to need no demonstration, but to be cognisable *a priori*. But we believe that this simplicity is only the stamp and evidence of its truth.
> (*37*, p. 399)

As it was expanded elsewhere in the book this law was not so simple. In its expanded form, it actually consisted of the following four propositions:

> 1 That the more general character of a large group of animals appears earlier in their embryos than the more special characters.
>
> With this it agrees perfectly that the vesicle should be the primitive form; for what can be a more general character of all animals than the contrast of an internal and an external suface?
>
> 2 From the most general forms the less general are developed, and so on, until finally the most special arises.
>
> This has been rendered manifest above by examples from the Vertebrate, especially of the Birds and also from the Articulata. We bring it forward again here only to append, as its immediate consequences, the following propositions concerning the object of investigation.
>
> 3 Every embryo of a given animal form, instead of passing through the other forms, rather becomes separated from them.
>
> 4 Fundamentally, therefore, the embryo of a higher form never resembles any other form, but only its embryo.
>
> It is only because the least developed forms of animals are but little removed from the embryonic condition that they retain a certain similarity to the embryo of higher forms of animals.
>
> This resemblance, however, if our view be correct, is nowise the determining condition of the course of development of the higher animals, but only a consequence of the organisation of the lower forms.

The development of the embryo with regard to type of organisation, is *as if it passed through the animal kingdom after the manner of the so-called methode analytique of the French systematists, continually separating itself from its allies*, and *at the same time* passing from a lower to a higher stage of development (*37*, p. 394, author's italics)

Von Baer represented the relationship he envisaged by a table which is reproduced on the opposite page. This is of interest for two reasons. Firstly, it shows more clearly than any description how far comparative embryology had progressed. Although von Baer himself rightly claimed that knowledge of this subject was still far from complete, it is astonishing that such a great advance should have been made during the first thirty years of the nineteenth century. Secondly, the table makes clear just what von Baer meant by his law, in a way that the propositions do not.

Von Baer's views on development were closely connected with his views on the structure of the animal kingdom. He denied all versions of the Great Chain of Being and accepted a form of the 'Archetype theory', according to which the forms of all animals were to be understood by reference to a limited number of ideal and fundamental patterns. Cuvier recognised four such 'ground plans', namely those of the Radiata, the Articulata, the Mollusca and the Vertebrata, and it would seem that von Baer's views were similar. Some animals were less modified than others, and von Baer's second proposition seems to suggest that the embryo, when it first shows itself as a member of a certain group, exhibits a form which almost approximates to the archetype. Von Baer's explanation and amplification of his law in terms of the Archetype theory is given in the following paragraph:

Furthermore the different forms of animals are sometimes more, sometimes less remote from the principal type. The type itself never exists pure, but only under certain modifications. But it seems absolutely necessary that those forms in which animality is most highly developed should be furthest removed from the fundamental type. In all the fundamental types, in fact, if I have discovered the true ones, there exists a symmetrical distribution of the organic elements. If now predominant central organs arise, especially a central part of the nervous system, according to which one must principally measure the extent of perfection, the type necessarily becomes considerably modified. The Worms, the Myriapoda, have an evenly annulated body, and are nearer the type than the Butterfly. If then the law be true, that in the course of development the principal type appears first, and subsequently

KARL ERNST VON BAER: SCHEME OF THE PROGRESS OF DEVELOPMENT

Lowest grade of development → Highest grade of development

The animal rudiment is either:

- a germ-granule (itself germ),
  - ? Radiate development . . . . *? Animals of the peripheral type*
  - Spiral development . . . . *Animals of the massive type*
  - Symmetrical development . . . . *Animals of the elongated type*
- or an ovum with a germ. In this arises:
  - Doubly symmetrical development . . . *Vertebrata.* They have a chorda dorsalis, dorsal plates, visceral plates, nerve tubes, gill-clefts, and acquire . . .
    - *Gills*
      - No true lungs formed
        - The skeleton does not ossify . . . . *Cartilaginous fishes*
        - The skeleton ossifies . . . . *Osseous fishes*
      - Lungs formed — *Amphibia*. The gills
        - persist . . . . *Sirenidae*
        - do not persist
          - remain external . . . . . . *Urodela*
          - become enclosed . . . . . . *Anura*
    - A much-developed allantois.
      - No umbilical cord
        - No wings nor air-sacs . . . . *Reptilia*
        - Wings and air-sacs . . . . *Aves*
      - An umbilical cord — *Mammalia*
        - which falls off early
          - without union with the parent? . . *Monotremata*
          - after a short union with the parent *Marsupialia*
        - which persists longer. The yelk-sac
          - grows for a long time. The allantois grows
            - very little . . . . *Rodentia*
            - moderately . . . . *Insectivora*
            - much . . . . *Carnivora*
          - grows little. The allantois grows
            - little . . . . *Quadrumana*
            - Umbilical cord very long . . . *Man*
            - very long. Placenta
              - in scattered masses . . . . *Ruminantia*
              - evenly distributed . . *Pachydermata*, *Cetacea*

As reproduced in A Source Book of Animal Biography, *Ed. T. Hall (by courtesy of the McGraw-Hill Book Company)*

its modifications, the young Butterfly must be more similar to the perfect Scolopendra and even to the perfect Worm, than conversely the young Scolopendra or the young Worm to the perfect Butterfly. . . . The same thing is obvious in the Vertebrata. Fishes are less distinct from the fundamental type than Mammalia, and especially than Man with his great brain. It is therefore very natural that the Mammalian embryo should be more similar to the Fish than the embryo of the Fish to the Mammal. (*37*, p. 396)

In his old age von Baer objected to Darwin's Theory of Natural Selection on the grounds that it was too materialistic. But whether he believed in any form of evolution is a matter which has been hotly debated. Certainly his final summing up of his work on embryology suggests that he did not, but rather than his view was similar to that of Oken (quoted above). For von Baer, after giving his law in its most general form, concluded in the following manner:

If, however, the general result which has just been expressed be well based and true, then there is *one* fundamental thought which runs through all forms and grades of animal development, and regulates all their peculiar relations. It is the same thought which collected the masses scattered through space into spheres, and united them into systems of suns; it is that which called forth into living forms the dust weathered from the surface of the metallic planet. But this thought is nothing less than Life itself, and the words and syllables in which it is expressed are the multitudinous forms of the Living. (*37*, p. 399)

In the course of his embryological investigations von Baer must have become familiar with the appearance of the very young mammalian embryo. One day, late in 1826, while examining the ovary of a bitch, von Baer 'accidentally' noticed an object within the Graafian follicle, which he recognised as a discrete body and therefore probably the mammalian egg. The St Petersburg Academy of Sciences was offering a prize for the best investigations on this matter, so von Baer immediately wrote a short account of his discovery in Latin, and sent it to Russia and to his publisher in Leipzig (*85*, a, Part II, p. 121). In 1828 he published a fuller German version of this work (*85*, b, and *53*, p. 90). Von Baer not only saw the eggs and described their formation, he gave detailed instructions for obtaining them, so that others could easily confirm his observations. It is clear that he saw and recognised the egg nucleus and that he had observed, without understanding, much of the early cleavage. Having studied the eggs of dogs, pigs, rabbits, and cats, he attempted to make a complete comparative study of the morphology of all eggs—birds, fishes and invertebrates included—which led him into considerable error. Nevertheless his study of the eggs themselves, and his patient attempt to obtain specimens of all the early stages of development, settled the main outlines of the process. It was a relatively simple task for subsequent investigators to apply the cell theory to these phenomena.

Von Baer saw the egg itself as the starting point for all future development, and he was able to connect the morphological differences he had observed with different types of early growth. But he was not interested in where fertilisation occurred nor how it was effected. What he had to say about fertilisation is interesting, for it highlights the difference between his approach and the attitude of either the eighteenth or the twentieth century biologist. He contrasted the 'wonderful, moving life in the seminal vesicles of the male frog' with the 'quiet majesty' of the egg in the germinal vesicle of the female animal. He hinted that the true secret of reproduction was hidden in this contrast, which was but a repetition of that contrast between the male and female nature which was manifest in other aspects of everyday life (*53*, p. 117 refers to p. 181 and p. 182 of the 'Commentary'). The circumstances of fertilisation and the nature of the contributions made by each sex are important for those who wish to give a causal explanation of generation. They are not so important if one is looking for generalised descriptions or phenomenological laws such as von Baer desired. The sexual act and the actual fertilisation are, from the latter point of view, seen as belonging to that class of facts which includes the essential differences between the male and female bodies, and the contrast in behaviour between the different sexes in all spheres and in all species—insects and man included.

Thus there was little connection between von Baer's embryological work and the eighteenth century investigations into generation. Von Baer and his predecessors of the German school approached the study of development with a completely different set of presuppositions. The new approach succeeded, and new facts were quickly accumulated. These new results would certainly have banished any hopes that further research would uncover the preformations of actual organs. But, as I have already shown, the late eighteenth century preformationists themselves did not believe that this would be possible. Preformation was retained during that period because of the need for a causal explanation of the phenomenon of gradual development. Von Baer offered no new explanatory hypothesis for differentiation because he regarded the whole idea of such explanations as absurd. It is for this reason that neither von Baer nor his German predecessors paid much attention to the theoretical discussions which had occurred in the previous century. They were certainly aware of some of the discoveries made at that time, but they admired and understood only the researches of Wolff and of Blumenbach, who approached the subject from a point of view similar to their own.

Most of von Baer's contemporaries accepted Serres' theory that each developing animal assumed, in ascending scale, the forms of all the lower types. Von Baer took this view seriously enough to be at pains to refute it. From his point of view, this law was incorrect, but it nevertheless constituted a genuine attempt to produce an explanation of the formal (i.e. morphological and historical) kind which he recognised. None of this group of German embryologists would have regarded their own work as a refutation of the preformation theory, for the simple reason that, from their point of view, not only the preformation theory but also the ideas of Maupertuis and of Buffon stemmed from a misguided and outmoded philosophy. Once this was seen, the ideas themselves required no further refutation.

Von Baer's own research increased the knowledge of comparative embryology enormously, but his example and his constant plea for more investigation had an even greater effect. Descriptive embryology became a popular subject which was naturally pursued along the lines laid down by its founder. The knowledge gained from these studies helped to establish the idea of evolution. Later the suggestions of Huxley and Haeckel further stimulated its growth. By 1885, Roux could declare:

> Since the end of the last century, descriptive embryology has, through the indefatigable industry and ingenuity of many investigators, been advanced to a point where, for almost every organ of the vertebrates, and many invertebrates, we know with a certain degree of exactness, the form changes through which, beginning with the fertilised egg, it progressively shapes itself.
> (*68*, and *37*, p. 412)

Von Baer's laws were set aside and other laws were formulated, but they were always morphological laws, concerned with a more generalised description of the forms through which the organism or organ passed. Von Baer had explained his laws by reference to the theory of archetypes; the later discoveries were explained by reference to the evolution of the plant or animal group. In a very real sense, embryology remained throughout the greater part of the nineteenth century wedded to the *kind* of explanation which had first appeared at the very beginning of the century. Throughout this long period, virtually no attempt was made to investigate the underlying material causes of these changes in form or to provide a causal account of development. Embryology therefore remained a distinct subject, completely separated from all other aspects of generation. It was not until 1885 that Roux re-established developmental mechanics, arguing that:

> After one has achieved an approximate survey of these changes of form during development, one is justified in taking a further step aimed at a knowledge of the processes which produce them.
> (*37*, p. 412)

Since Roux's time much research has been directed to this end, and embryology has tended to become once again more closely connected with other studies of generation.

14
Conclusion

'Out of date theories are not, in principle, unscientific because they have been discarded.'

Kuhn, STRUCTURE OF SCIENTIFIC REVOLUTION

MOST histories of science are success stories which conclude on a triumphal note with the acceptance of a theory that is the basis of our modern enquiries in the selected field. This history has no such triumphal ending. By the end of the period we have studied there was more despondency about ever solving the central problems of generation than there had been in the beginning. Indeed, this despondency was so great that, for some considerable time, the whole project was almost abandoned.

There was a further cause of the virtual abandonment of the subject; this was the change in metaphysical outlook, described in the last chapter, which removed both the urge and the need to understand the inner processes of growth and development. Why look for something which many, being vitalists, claimed was impossible to find, and why bother about this aspect of biology if the majority were prepared to say simply that it was the manifestation of the vital spirit? These very general changes in attitude do not have much influence on scientific enquiries which have achieved a well established and fruitful theoretical basis. In these cases the change may affect the direction taken by peripheral regions of study and may alter the general assessment of the importance of a subject, giving it a greater or lesser effect on the intellectual life of the times. But those who are actually working in the field will continue to work within the framework of their successful theory.

The romantic movement and the attendant nature philosophy had a profound effect on early nineteenth century biology because, as a whole, the subject still lacked any satisfactory theoretical framework. The attempts to apply the mechanical and atomistic models to a large number of different topics had met with only limited success. The new outlook, with its insistence on generalised descriptions and explanations in terms of a historical sequence of forms, helped to start many fruitful lines of investigation, of which descriptive embryology was a typical example, and in many cases important advances were made. So it is not surprising that biologists pursued these new studies and did not return to some of the old problems which, like generation, had seemed so central to the discipline in the seventeenth and eighteenth centuries, but which had proved so intractable.

The 'mechanistic' approach to physiological problems reappeared about the middle of the nineteenth century, but it was not until some thirty years later that investigators, such as Roux, started to enquire into the mechanics of animal development. By 'mechanistic approach' I mean one which attempts to explain vital phenomena in terms of inner processes, in the hope that these can ultimately be completely explained in terms of physical and chemical changes. An interest in inheritance had, of course, reappeared earlier in the context of the evolutionary theory. When, in 1859, Darwin suggested in *The Origin of Species* that evolution could have occurred as the result of a natural process he incidentally revived an interest in this topic. His main concern was to suggest that the total environment acting on the individual organisms tended to ensure that, on the average, the variants best suited to their conditions would survive and leave the most offspring, so that the types themselves would be gradually modified. The analogy was with the human breeders who, by deliberate selection, could produce new kinds of animals and plants. But, as Darwin freely acknowledged, this was only part of the story. While there was abundant evidence that breeders could alter their stock, no one had any idea of the laws governing the production and transmission of those variations which provided the raw material with which the breeders worked.

Whether or not natural selection itself was accepted as the chief method by which evolution was achieved, any attempt to account for the process by natural means must inevitably include a knowledge of the laws governing the inheritance of minor variations. Herbert Spencer was amongst the first to realise this and his account of evolution, which appeared in his *Principles of Biology* (published in 1864 and in 1869), included what was virtually a complete theory of generation. In 1868, Darwin published *The Variations of Animals and Plants under Domestication* in which he suggested his hypothesis of pangenesis. Both Spencer's theory of physiological units and Darwin's theory of pangenesis were very reminiscent of the theories of generation which had been produced a hundred years before. Both covered the same range of phenomena and both were very speculative. They differed from the eighteenth century's theories in two respects. Since they were produced as part of an attempt to account for evolution, their emphasis was on the transmission of variations and not in the preservation of type. Secondly, although neither Spencer nor Darwin were familiar with the details of the cell theory, both authors assumed that the parental contributions to the new organism were cells or cellular structures.

Gradually, during the latter part of the nineteenth century, more and more biologists accepted evolution as a fact and concentrated their attention upon the question of what processes could possibly bring it about. In all cases this forced them, as it had forced Spencer and Darwin, to consider the relevant aspects of generation. The laws governing the inheritance of minor differences now became a matter of considerable importance, and breeding experiments and statistical investigations were undertaken in many different centres.

It was at this time that the details of cell division and reduction division were established. At last the formation of the gametes and their ultimate fusion were observed and understood, within the framework of the cell theory. Suddenly a great number of different theories of generation were suggested, all with the intention of explaining the inner and organic aspect of the evolutionary process. These varied greatly in what they assumed about the inheritance of variations and also in their cognisance of the new advances in cytology. Some, like Weismann's ultimate views, were complete theories of generation which postulated a variety of intra-cellular particles and which aimed at explaining all the phenomena of inheritance, reproduction, growth and differentiation in terms of the more recent developments in the cell theory. Other more limited theories were simply concerned with the inheritance of the variations themselves.

In 1901 Mendel's laws were rediscovered and his original paper which contained his explanatory theory was at last read and appreciated. These events marked the beginnings of modern genetics. Of course, as is usual in all fruitful investigations, the application of Mendel's laws has undergone a series of modifications and his theory itself has been considerably modified. During the first two decades of the twentieth century, the predominant interest in biology still continued to be the evolutionary process itself. Mendelism (genetics) created great interest because a knowledge of heredity was essential to an understanding of evolution. In 1930 Sir Ronald Fisher could still say:

> In the future, the revolutionary effects of Mendelism will be seen to flow from the particulate character of the hereditary elements. On this fact a rational theory of Natural Selection can be based and it is therefore of enormous importance.
> (*28*)

Since evolution is accepted as part of the framework of modern biology, any investigation which can throw light on the process by which it has been achieved will be important. But in the last fifty years the principal aims of genetics have undergone a gradual change and I doubt if many modern geneticists would agree wholeheartedly with Sir Ronald's prediction.

This change has been brought about by the acceptance of the chromosome theory of heredity. Immediately the Mendelian theory became known, a parallel was noted between the behaviour of the chromosomes at the formation of the sex cells and the postulated behaviour of the Mendelian factors. By 1919, when Morgan published *The Physical Basis of Heredity*, a true connection was finally established. As a result of this, it became possible to link some of the features exhibited by the mature organisms with the content and structure of the sex cells and eventually to use breeding experiments as a tool to probe into the vital processes themselves. In the subsequent period this aspect of modern genetics has come to occupy a more and more central position in research. In 1954, Stadler summarised these new aims as follows:

> The central problem of biology is the physical nature of living substance. It is this which gives drive and zest to the study of the gene, the investigation of genic substance seems at present our most direct approach to this problem.
> (*74*)

Professor Pontecorvo recognised the change which had taken place within genetics even more clearly when he remarked:

> Clearly, if we are to free ourselves of the fetters of formal genetics, of genetics based on abstractions—of genetics as merely the mechanics of hereditary transmission, there is no doubt that we have to give physical, chemical and physiological content to the processes of heredity, variation and differentiation. We have to express such concepts as gene, allele, mutation, crossing over dominance, etc. in terms of precise processes taking place in or on structures of the cell.
> (*62*, p. 4)

In so far as this is now the main objective, genetics has become a true study of generation. We share the general aim—to give a causal account of all the phenomena of development in terms of the original parental donations—which motivated the seventeenth century preformationists and the eighteenth century workers like Maupertuis and Buffon. The failure of these investigators has not been absolute, for while twentieth century genetics has still not achieved complete success, it has made a most promising and exciting beginning. It is, of course, a recognition of this similarity of aim and outlook which makes a study of the seventeenth and eighteenth century investigations so interesting for the modern geneticist.

But while modern genetics is, logically, the successful heir to the seventeenth and eighteenth century investigations into generation, there is not much historical connection between the two enquiries. The gap during the early nineteenth century was too great. When a successful new metaphysical outlook appears the proponents of the new approach are usually very unwilling to see much virtue in the work of their immediate predecessors against whom they are in revolt. The seventeenth century physicists gave no hint of the work which had been done by the scientists in the middle ages, and in the same way the early nineteenth century biologists made a complete break with the past. Very occasionally, workers like von Baer discussed the experimental discoveries and observations made by seventeenth and eighteenth century biologists. But since they regarded the theoretical approach of their forerunners as completely misguided, and since the new outlook directed attention to completely different questions, there was indeed little continuity.

When, later in the nineteenth century, some of the old problems reappeared, most scientists were completely ignorant of any earlier theories. But at the same time there had been a very great deal of progress in other fields. Thus the late nineteenth century biologists were able to employ many of the new discoveries made in the interim. For example, Darwin was surprised when he was told that his theory of pangenesis was very similar to certain Greek views. He was completely unaware of the seventeenth and eighteenth century controversies about generation. Yet it is difficult to see, in the changed biological climate, that a knowledge of earlier ideas would have been any real help to him.

During the period of chaos and theoretical confusion which occurred at the end of the nineteenth century, some scientists did take an interest in the eighteenth century work on generation. Thomas Huxley wrote about it in his more general biological essays. Whitman gave a number of lectures on Charles Bonnet (*96*, a) and Wheeler discussed Wolff's work (*95*). A fairly complete historical survey was given by Delage at the beginning of his book on heredity (*18*). In the main, these historical studies were used as an introduction to a discussion of the author's own views. The older theories had little direct influence. Indeed, it was the differences in outlook which were stressed. At the end of the nineteenth century it was the inheritance of variations which interested the biologists who were concerned with the mechanisms of evolution. Apart from Maupertuis, the eighteenth century writers had assumed a continuity of type and were chiefly interested in the process of differentiation and in the exact contributions made by the two sexes. Starting as they did from such different points of view, it is little wonder that the nineteenth century biologists dismissed the earlier theories as mere historical curiosities. Today, when our own studies combine both approaches, we take a more sympathetic view of the earlier endeavours.

The seventeenth and eighteenth century biologists failed to establish a successful theory of generation and, as a result, their investigations had little effect on the development of modern views. In the preceding chapters I have tried to analyse the situation in detail and to show how the known facts and the ideas on what constituted a satisfactory explanation influenced each individual worker's conclusions. But can anything more general be added to this review? Can one say that in all these diverse cases there was one factor above all others which prevented further progress?

Some seventeenth and eighteenth century workers, like Descartes and Maupertuis, wished to give an account of generation in which all the phenomena were explained in terms of physical and chemical processes. In so far as this was their aim, failure was inevitable. No matter how successful their biological investigations had been, this would have been impossible for non-biological reasons. It is obvious that a necessary—but not a sufficient—condition for such an enterprise is a well developed chemistry. Retrospectively it is quite clear that the chemistry of the period was hopelessly inadequate for the task. Our present knowledge is only just sufficient to meet the demands made upon it by the modern science of genetics, yet this modern subject cannot claim to have achieved the aims of these early optimists.

The majority of the seventeenth and eighteenth century workers had a more limited and a more specifically biological aim: they hoped to explain all the attendant phenomena associated with reproduction in terms of the initial primordium. In the case of sexual reproduction they also hoped to explain the primordium in terms of the parental contributions. Here it does seem that there was one major obstacle. It is almost tautological to say that if they had developed some version of the cell theory many of their difficulties would have disappeared and the preformation theory would not have persisted until the end of the eighteenth century. Professor Cole, as a result of his intensive study of the period, concluded:

> It [the preformation theory] enjoyed a life of well over a century. It is true its life would have been curtailed but for the slow development of microscopic techniques and the belated appearance of the cell theory.
> (*11*, p. 203)

In so far as Professor Cole is simply stating that the chief obstacle to progress in this field was the lack of the cell theory he is obviously correct. In the quotation, however, Professor Cole refers to 'the slow development' of microscopic techniques and the 'belated' appearance of the cell theory. Elsewhere in his concluding chapter he suggests that more progress could have been made and, indeed, that the cell theory might have been developed if the eighteenth century workers had paid more attention to their observations and spent less time in formulating speculative theories. It is often possible for historians of science to show that a given line of enquiry failed because the investigators lacked an essential fact or theory, which was only supplied later. It is generally more difficult even to think of the sort of evidence which might be produced to establish or disprove the claim that it should have been possible for the workers of a certain period to have made advances which they in fact failed to make. In this particular case, however, there is some evidence which strongly suggests that, while the eighteenth century workers were handicapped by the lack of the cell theory, their failure to formulate the theory was in no way due to a mistaken scientific procedure but rather to factors beyond their control.

Theoretically many of the investigators considered in the earlier chapters came very near to the formal recognition of a basic physiological unit. The physicists of the period believed that all the properties of inanimate matter would finally be explained in terms of its ultimate particles.

At the time, however, they could do little to substantiate this claim. In a like manner, the biologists who favoured the particulate theories of generation assumed that there must be a basic vital unit. In all cases it was assumed that this basic unit must be responsible for the inheritance of the parental characteristics, must be capable of self-duplication and that it must control both growth and differentiation. Views on the composition of the vital units differed. Maupertuis thought, as we do, that these units must be unique combinations of the fundamental inanimate atoms, whereas Buffon thought that they must be combinations of special animate particles.

The more sophisticated preformationists altered their ideas about the preformed germs in the light of their discoveries. As their knowledge grew the germs became progressively more widespread within the organisms and the preformation became less clearly defined. By the end of the eighteenth century preformation was little more than a power to determine subsequent development.

In the light of what they had learnt about reproduction and regeneration all these theorists were led towards somewhat similar conclusions. Far from leading them astray, their speculations, in the light of the known facts, led them towards an inferred physiological and reproductive unit. These are important aspects of the cell theory, but what they lacked was the knowledge of any structural unit with which they could link their inferences.

There are a number of obvious reasons why the eighteenth century anatomists failed to recognise the cell as the basic structural unit. Some of these reasons are concerned with the development of the microscope itself. The miscroscopes of this period were poor, they probably varied greatly, they were few in number and difficult to obtain. It was not until the nineteenth century that an improved achromatic version of the compound microscope was manufactured in sufficient quantities and at a price which enabled a number of workers to engage in microscopic investigations.

That virtually all living material is organised into cells is a generalisation which is based on investigations into many different kinds of plants and animals. It is not the type of generalisation which can be made or accepted until a large number of people have moderately reliable instruments with which to undertake microscopic investigations. Even after its initial formulation, the cell theory developed very slowly because of handicaps of this kind.

A study of plant material is perhaps most likely to lead investigators towards a cell theory. Hooke originally introduced the term 'cell' when he was investigating the microscopic appearance of cork, but but he also noted that similar pores, some with a liquid content, could be seen in other parts of plants. Seventeenth century workers, Grew, Malpighi and Leeuwenhoek, came nearest to the cell theory in their botanical investigations. But plant anatomy was not popular in the eighteenth century; the botanists were concerned with problems of classification, while biologists with more general interests gave their attention to the animal kingdom.

In spite of all these difficulties individual workers sometimes saw and described cells. Swammerdam saw the two-cell stage in the development of the tadpole. Trembley and Spallanzani both observed the multiplication of unicellular organisms by cell division. But these isolated cases, although they were accurately described, were without any significance since neither the observers nor their contemporaries had the experience necessary to see them as examples of an important generalisation.

Some progress was made in the understanding of the organisation of animals but, ironically, this progress had the effect of directing attention away from the cell. The seventeenth century anatomists concentrated their attention upon the organs of animals but, as knowledge increased, they gradually realised that these organs appeared to be composed of a limited number of distinct materials which could be recognised in a large number of different animals. They called these materials 'textures' or 'tissues'. (The French word 'tissu' = a woven fabric; the Latin word used by Haller, 'tela' = a web or a woven material.) Today the term 'tissue' indicates an assemblage of more or less independent cells, and the analogy between this assemblage and a fabric is completely lost. For the eighteenth century physiologists it was very real, within many of the 'textures' they could see solid fibres which appeared to interweave. Just as we distinguish different fabrics by their patterns so they distinguished these textures. Thus 'cellular tissues' or 'cellular textures' indicated a type of material which had a pitted appearance just as, today, 'cellular cotton' is a cotton material with an open weave. Haller's work on muscles and some of the work done on nerves tended to give the impression that the 'tissues' or the fibres from which they believed they were formed were both the structural and the physiological elements of all animals. In 1802 Bichat formulated one version of this theory. But though the 'tissues' might be plausible candidates for the role of structural and physiological elements it was difficult to make them into reproductive units. As we have seen, Rolando and Dumas attempted to do this, and it involved them in a kind of preformation theory which was different from the original but hardly more satisfactory.

This very short summary of the seventeenth and eighteenth century biologists' attitude to vital organisation does show that they were deeply concerned with the problem. This concern is also apparent in all their work on generation. Everything we know about the conditions of this period and about the steps which led to ultimate formulation of the cell theory seems to suggest that their inability to arrive at any approximation to a cell theory was due to factors over which they had no control. But if this is so, then, in the last analysis, their inability to make any decisive progress in the study of generation was likewise due to such factors.

Nevertheless, almost all commentators, including Professor Cole, have condemned the seventeenth and eighteenth century investigations into generation as 'too speculative' and have said that they showed 'that fatal preoccupation with philosophy which prefers the science of words to the austerities of serious research' (*11*, pp. 198–9). Just what is meant by these criticisms? We might say that a subject was 'too speculative' if the whole discussion was based on assumptions which were unverified or only supported by the most casual observations but the work on generation does not fall into this category. The investigations of Harvey, Malpighi and de Graaf were amongst the most careful empirical enquiries conducted during the period. If the subject was 'too speculative' the criticism must refer either to the theories suggested as a result of this work or to the inter-connections between these theories and the subsequent investigations.

A theory might be described as too speculative because the assumptions it made seem absurd. To the modern reader there is nothing absurd in assuming that the formation of a new organism is determined by inorganic particles, which was what Maupertuis assumed. Nor is there anything absurd about Buffon's suggestion that all living things were built up from vital particles; we do not believe this but neither do we find the idea implausible. On the other hand, the assumption that the first parent contained within it the germs of all future generations seems absolutely absurd. It is natural to judge such theories by their plausibility for us, but, from the historical point of view, this is often a mistake. In the first place, during the seventeenth and eighteenth centuries a large number of new discoveries were made against a background of incomplete knowledge. As a result there was little ability to distinguish between the probable and the improbable in any field. Secondly, the biology of the time lacked both the cell theory and the idea of evolution, so that the background thought on this subject was very different from ours. In order to decide if the assumptions of a theory seemed plausible at the time we can only examine the historical evidence. We can see if the theory was criticised as being implausible at the time and discover what weight was attached to the criticisms. We find, in fact, that Hartsoeker did calculate the number of germs which must have been present in the first rabbit and abandoned preformation on the grounds of his result. But there is no evidence that this criticism was regarded as in any way conclusive by his contemporaries. In such a case when contemporary opinion differs very much from ours, all we can do is to re-examine the situation and try to understand why the theory appeared acceptable in that particular historical context.

A theory might be called speculative not because of the nature of the assumptions, but because of the connection or lack of connection between the theory and the known facts. Some historians seem to have assumed that the theories which seventeenth and eighteenth century scientists proposed in their investigations into generation were mere working hypotheses that could be directly verified or refuted by observation or experiment. None of the theories were of this nature for all were clearly formulated to explain the known facts. In this respect they had the same logical status as most modern theories. It is not usually thought necessary that each separate assumption made in such a theory should be capable of independent verification. It is the inferences from the theory as a whole which are to be checked against, and which must accord with, the facts. How far can we say that the seventeenth and eighteenth century investigations met these requirements?

1 The earliest version of preformation was certainly adequate for the meagre facts which required explanation. These were the discoveries of Harvey and de Graaf which seemed to indicate that the female contribution to sexual reproduction was in the form of some sort of egg produced within the ovary, and the observations of Harvey and Malpighi on embryo development. In order to explain these phenomena it was assumed that the preformed germ was in the ovum, and that it was the gradual increase in size and increase in solidification of this germ which gave rise to the appearance of epigenetic development.

2 The animalculism, suggested as the result of the discovery of the spermatozoa, gave a good explanation of sexual reproduction which accorded with all the discoveries; but it did not accord with the embryological facts. Since the spermatozoa were plainly alive before they entered the eggs they must, according to the ideas of the time, have organs. It was these organs which expanded into those of the adult organism. Here the preformation was more real and it was difficult to account for the appearance of epigenesis. It was this clash between the theory and the embryological facts which contributed to its abandonment. The young Haller rejected animalculism for this reason, and when Maupertuis and Buffon claimed that preformation was not in accord with the facts of enbryology it was this more popular version which they probably had in mind.

3 The particulate theories, suggested in the mid-eighteenth century, all denied that the female contribution to the new organism was a discrete body. They were, therefore, in conflict with the discoveries of Harvey and de Graaf. Again it was this, together with

the fact that they gave no better explanation of embryo development, which forced the late eighteenth century workers back to ovism.

4 Bonnet attempted to modify this version of preformation so as to accommodate all the known facts. It was the work on animal regeneration which caused him to suggest that the germs were not limited to the female sex organs but were spread throughout the organisms. What was known as hybrid and biparental inheritance gave rise to his subsidiary theory of biparental nutrition.

On this minimum requirement of accordance with known fact these theories pass the test. In all cases they were either abandoned or altered once a clash with any part of the very complicated range of phenomena was noted. But a theory must do more than explain the phenomena. To be regarded as satisfactory it must be capable of stimulating enquiries by suggesting new research. Did these theories of generation play any part in directing research, or were they so ill formed as to be useless in this respect? In general, there is no doubt that the difficult enquiries into generation were kept alive because of the theoretical conflicts. In a more direct way, the different theories were responsible for a number of empirical enquiries. Without attempting a comprehensive survey, the following cases come to mind:

1 The numerous investigations into the origin of certain of the invertebrata (e.g. the gall flies) were due to the fact that the preformationists could not believe in spontaneous generation. In this case the theory led to the correct interpretation of the facts.

2 Needham's initial investigations into the infusoria were undertaken at the request of Buffon, who was already thinking about the theory of the vital particles. Here faulty techniques and theoretical commitment produced a completely erroneous interpretation of his results.

3 Much of Spallanzani's work on generation had a theoretical origin. He repeated Needham's experiments on the infusoria in order to disprove Buffon's theory. His work on the semen was undertaken at Bonnet's request and misinterpreted for theoretical

reasons. His unsuccessful attempts to stimulate the growth of eggs by chemical and physical means was the direct result of an inference from the current ovism.

4 The interest in plant hybrids stemmed from Linnaeus' theory of the origin of species, but the interest in 'monsters' and in animal hybrids was generally the result of the conflicts between the different theories of sexual reproduction. Maupertuis' remarkable investigations into human inheritance were undertaken as a result of his theory.

5 Both Wolff's and Haller's work on embryo development was directly linked with their theoretical interest in generation which preceded their empirical investigations.

Thus it is plain that, however speculative these theories of generation were, there was a genuine, if often unsuccessful, attempt to relate them to the phenomena and test them by empirical enquiry.

In fact, on the criteria mentioned so far, the theories seem to have little wrong with them. In some respects, however, they were unsatisfactory and speculative. We cannot stipulate how many assumptions a theory may have, nor can we give any ratio between the number of assumptions and the range of facts to be explained, but clearly there are limits here. To take an absurd example—if a theory contains an enormous number of assumptions and if we have to tell a very long story in order to explain one single experiment, then the theory is unsatisfactory, uneconomical, lacking in simplicity or 'too speculative'. It is the clumsiness of these speculations about generation which is one of the major faults. All theories get more complicated as the range of evidence increases and, in most cases, the assumptions of the hypotheses have to be altered to accommodate some of the new discoveries. But a theory is unsatisfactory if it has to be altered in order to include each new fact and if elaborate new hypotheses must be formed. Again, these theories, particularly the ovist version of preformation which had the longest life, had to be changed too frequently.

We have already seen that the investigations into generation could not make decisive progress without the cell theory. In such a situation there are two alternatives open to the investigators. They can record their initial researches which give rise to the problems and then simply refrain from any speculation. Such a course does not usually stimulate research. Some progress may be made at the descriptive level, as new facts are noted in the course of other investigations. But even these facts tend to be overlooked since, if this attitude prevails, the subject as a central theme for investigation soon ceases to exist. Alternatively, they can suggest explanatory theories which will inevitably be very speculative. The subject will remain as a subject, but the theory or theories will tend to direct enquiries into unprofitable channels. The facts discovered may be misinterpreted and time may be spent in useless controversies. Nevertheless, if the second alternative is chosen, research will continue, knowledge will be gained, interest will be maintained and some progress will be made—as it was in these studies.

Time Chart

History of Generation

1651 HARVEY:
All living things start as primordia. Viviparous generation is analogous to oviparous.

1656 WHARTON:
Semen might mix with female secretion in the 'female testicles' in mammals.

1658 GASSENDI:
Essay on the Formation of Foetus. (Published posthumously.)

1665 DESCARTES:
On the Formation of the Foetus. (Latin version 1662—both posthumous.)

1668 VAN HORNE:
'Hydatid vesicles' in the female testicles are the true ova of mammals.

1669 SWAMMERDAM:
First published reference to the 'Preformation Theory'.

1671 KERCKRING:
'Female testicles' in mammals are the equivalent to ovaries in birds and also produce ova.

1672 SWAMMERDAM:
Fuller account of the Preformation Theory in work which also discusses the function of the ovaries in mammals.

1672 DE GRAAF:
Confirms the analogy between oviparous and viviparous reproduction. Describes changes in 'hydatid vesicles Graafian follicles) which are associated with conception.

1672–3–5 MALPIGHI:
Detailed description of early stages of the chick embryo.

1674 MALEBRANCHE:
Discusses preformation in *De la recherche de la vérité.*

1678 HUYGENS:
Describes spermatozoa as seen by Leeuwenhoek.

1679 LEEUWENHOEK:
Letter (dated 1677) describing spermatozoa published in *Phil. Trans.*

1682 GREW:
Suggests plants also reproduce sexually.

1683 LEEUWENHOEK:
Animalculist version of preformation.

1684 REDI:
Maggots, etc., do not arise spontaneously in meat.

1683–1708 Animalculism increases in popularity.

1694 CAMERARIUS:
Plant sexuality established.

1700 ANDRY:
On Worms in the Human Body. Spermatozoa given animalculist interpretation.

1703 MORELAND:
Animalculist theory applied to plants.

1719 BRADLEY:
Suggests hybrid origin of some garden plants.

1719 MARCHANT:
New varieties of mercuralis appear in garden—are they new species?

1725–40 LEMERY and WINSLOW:
Dispute about the explanation of monsters.

1735 LINNAEUS:
Publishes first version of his classification.

1740–4 TREMBLEY:
The regenerative power and nature of polyps.

1744 MAUPERTUIS:
First essay on generation.

1745 BONNET:
Confirms Leeuwenhoek's belief in parthenogenesis in lice.

1745 MAUPERTUIS:
Vénus Physique.

1748 BUFFON:
First publication of his theory of generation.

1749 TURBERVILLE NEEDHAM:
Observations on infusions.

1749 RÉAUMUR:
Methods of incubation of domestic fowls. Discussion of ideas on generation. Pedigree of Kalleia family.

1751–2 MAUPERTUIS:
Système de la nature.
Letters: pedigree of Ruhe family.

1751 HALLER:
Reflections on Buffon's theory of generation.

1758 HALLER:
Conversion to preformation.

1759 WOLFF:
Theoria Generationis.

1760 LINNAEUS:
The monograph on plant sexuality containing a discussion on hybrids as the originators of new species.

1762 BONNET:
Publishes first version of preformation theory.

1761–6 KOELREUTER:
Investigations into plant hybridisation.

1764–5 BONNET:
Contemplation de la Nature.

1765 SPALLANZANI:
Investigations into the infusions.

1766 HALLER:
Elementa Physiologiae.

1768 SPALLANZANI:
Work on regeneration and conversion to preformation.

1768–9 WOLFF:
Later work on the development of the kidneys and intestines.

1769 BONNET:
Palingenesis.

1780 SPALLANZANI:
Work on the nature of the semen and artificial insemination.

1797 CRUIKSHANK:
'Ova' of rabbits seen in fallopian tubes three days after copulation.

1799–1823 KNIGHT:
Investigates the practical possibilities of plant hybridisation.

1802 BICHAT:
Theory of tissues.

1823 ROLANDO:
The spermatozoon supplies the nervous system, the ovum contains other systems.

1824 PRÉVOST and DUMAS:
Experiments on semen and fertilisation almost identify the mammalian egg.

1824 GOSS and SETON:
Note the segregation of blue and white seeds in the first generation bred from hybrid.

1827 DUMAS:
Theory of generation similar to Rolando.

1827 VON BAER:
Discovery of mammalian egg.

1828–37 VON BAER:
Embryological works.

1838–9 SCHLEIDEN and SCHWANN:
The Cell Theory.
Schwann—the egg is probably a cell.

1839–49 The parasite interpretation of the spermatozoa still has wide currency.

1849 WAGNER and LEUCKART:
Spermatozoa are definite and essential part of semen—the liquid merely keeps them in suspension. Contact between the spermatozoon and ovum initiates new development.

1859 DARWIN:
Origin of Species.

1864 SPENCER:
Theory of heredity via the 'physiological units'.

1865–7 NAEGELI:
Work on Hieracium classification and hybridisation.

1865–84 NAEGELI:
The development of the theory of the idioplasm.

1866 MENDEL:
Hybridisation of peas, etc.—the laws and theory of inheritance.

1868 DARWIN:
Variations of Animals and Plants under Domestication: The theory of pangenesis—'pangens' from cells of the parents influence the development of equivalent cells in offspring.

1869 MENDEL:
Conclusion of Hieracium experiments.

1869 HOFFMANN:
Mentions Mendel's work on peas in his own work on the selection of varieties.

1865–89 GALTON:
Investigations into the inheritance of human characteristics by statistical methods.

1872–1900 The inheritance of acquired characteristics questioned by Galton and Weismann. Gradual increase of doubt about all examples.

1869–93 Experiments by Brown-Séquard.

1875 O. Hertwig sees fertilisation in sea urchins.

1879 Fol observes spermatozoon penetrating egg.
Van Beneden: reduction of number of chromosomes in gametes in Ascaris.

1881 FOCKE:
Mentioned Mendel's work in famous book on Plant Hybridisation.

1883 VAN BENEDEN et alii:
The chromosomes must be material basis for inheritance.

1887 WEISMAN:
Theory of the germ plasm.

1887 DE VRIES:
Starts investigations into discontinuous variations called by him mutations.

1889 DE VRIES:
Intracellular pangenesis.

1894 BATESON:
Small continuous variations are not raw material for evolution.

1900 Rediscovery of Mendel's law and discovery of Mendel's paper.
de Vries — March
Correns — April
Tschermak — June.

1901–3 DE VRIES:
Mutation Theory.

1903 SUTTON:
Chromosomes and heredity.

1903 JOHANNSEN:
Pure lines in a mixed population.

1902–5 MCCLUNG, WILSON and others:
Sex chromosomes discovered.

1908 BATESON and PUNNET
Linkage in sweet peas.

1908 HARDY, WEINBERG:
Law linking Mendelian hypothesis with population studies.

1909 JANSSENS:
Suggests Chiasma Theory and its connection with the transfer of genetic substances.

1910–15 MORGAN, BRIDGES, etc:
Chromosome Theory of Heredity.

Bibliography

1 Andry de Boisregard, N. *De la Génération des Vers dans le Corps de l'Homme*. Paris, 1700

2 Aristotle *On the Soul*. Ed. W. Hett. Book 2, Section I, 412 B. Loeb Edition, Heinemann, 1948

3 Aromataria, Joseph of *Epistola de Generatione Plantarum ex Seminibus*. Venice, 1625. Translated in *Philosophical Transactions* of the Royal Society. Vol. XVIII, 1694

4 Bartholinus, C. *De Ovariis Mulierum*. Rome, 1677

5 Beaglehole, J. C. *The Endeavour Journal of Sir Joseph Banks*. Angus & Robertson. Sydney, 1962

6 Bichat, M. F. X. *Anatomie Général Appliquée à la Physiologie et la Medicine*. Paris, 1801. (See also Hayward's translation in No. *37*)

7 Boerhaave, H. *Praelectiones Academicae* with notes and additions by A. von Haller. Vol. V. Goettingen, 1744

8 Bonnet, C. *Œuvres Complètes* (in 17 vols.). Neuchatel, 1799. (Vols. I–X published 1779 as: *Œuvres d'Histoire Naturelle et de Philosophie*)
(a) 'Observations sur les Pucerons'. Vol. I, p. 1 ff. 1774. (First published in 1745 as *Traité d'Insectologie*)
(b) 'Observations sur quelques Espèces de Vers'. Vol. I, p. 167 ff. 1750. (Containing *Dissertation sur la Taenia* first published in 1750)
(c) 'Recherches sur l'Usage des Feuilles dans les Plantes'. Vol. I, p. 17 ff. 1760
(d) 'Considérations sur les Corps Organisés'. Vol. V, p. 83 ff. 1762
(e) 'Contemplation de la Nature'. Parts I and II, Vols. VIII and IX. 1764–6
(f) 'Palingénésie'. 22 parts. Parts I–XI, Vol XV, parts XI–XXII, Vol. XVI. 1770

9 Bradley, R. (a) *New Improvements of Planting and Gardening*. Ed. London, 1718
(b) *The Works of Nature*, London, 1721

10 Camerarius, R. 'De Sexu Plantarum'. *Academicae Caesareo Leopold*, Vol. VIII. Tübingen, 1694

11 Cole, F. J. *Early Theories of Sexual Generation.* Oxford University Press, 1930

12 Croone, W. 'De Formatione Pulli in Ovo'. *Philosophical Transactions* of the Royal Society, Vol. VII. 1672

13 Cruikshank, W. 'Experiments in which the Ova of Rabbits Were Found in the Fallopian Tubes'. *Philosophical Transactions* of the Royal Society. No. 87. 1797

14 Dalenpatius *Nouvelles de la République des Lettres.* Art. 5. Amsterdam, 1699

15 —— *History of the Works of the Learned.* Vol. I. London, 1699

16 de Buffon, C. L. *Histoire Naturelle.* (Vol. II, 'Des Animaux' is used for reference.) Sonnini-Dupont. Paris, 1749

17 de Graaf, René *De Mulierum Organis Generationi Inservientibus Tractatus Novus.* Leiden, 1672

18 Delage, Y. *L'Hérédité et les Grandes Problèmes de la Biologie Générale.* 3rd Ed. Schleichen Fr. Paris, 1903

19 de Maupertuis, P. L. M. *Vénus Physique.* Paris, 1745 and '56. (Here the 1756 edition is used for reference)
(a) Part I: 'Une Dissertation Physique à l'Occasion de Nègre Blanc'. (Original French version, 1744)
(b) Part II: 'Une Dissertation sur l'Origine des Noirs'

20 —— *Système de la Nature.* Erlangen, 1757

21 —— *Lettres de M. de Maupertuis.* Dresden, 1751

22 de Réaumur, R. A. F. *L'Histoire des Insectes.* Paris, 1734

23 —— (a) *Art de Faire Éclore et d'Élever en Toute Saison des Oiseaux Domestiques de Toutes Espèces.* Vol II. Paris, 1749
(b) English Translation A. Trembley. London, 1750

24 Descartes, R. (a) *L'Homme et* (b) *Un Traité de la Formation de Foetus.* Latin version, ed. Schmyl, Leiden, 1662. (French version 1664, and as Vol. II, Edition Nationale of Descartes' work: Adam and Tannery, Paris, 1909.)

25 Dobell, C. *Antony von Leeuwenhoek and His Little Animals.* Dale Danielsson, London, 1932

26 Dumas, J. B. and Prévost, J. L. 'Sur les Animalcules Spermatiques de divers Animaux'. *Memoires Société Physique.* Vol. I. Geneva, 1821

27 —— 'Nouvelles Theories de la Generation'
Annales des Sciences Naturelles
(a) Vols. I and II. Paris, 1824
(b) Vol. III. Paris, 1824
(c) Vol. IV. Paris, 1825
(d) Vol. VII. Paris, 1825
(e) Vol. XII. Paris, 1827.

28 Fisher, R. A. *The Genetical Theory of Natural Selection.* Oxford, Clarendon Press, 1930

29 Garden, C. 'On the Modern Theory of Generation'. *Philosophical Transactions* of the Royal Society. Vol. XVII, No. 192. 1691

30 Gassendi, P. Essay in *Opera Omnia.* Lyon, 1658

31 Geoffroy, E. 'Table des Differens . . .'
Mémoires de L'Academie des Sciences. Paris, 1718

32 Gerber, F. *Handbuch der Allgemeinen Anatomie des Menschen.* Berlin, 1840

33 Glass, Bentley, Ed., with Temkin, O. and Strauss, J. *Forerunners of Darwin.* John Hopkins Press. Baltimore, 1959

34 Goss, J. and Seton, A. 'On Variation in the Colour of Peas Occasioned by Cross-Impregnation'. *Transactions of the Horticultural Society.* London, 1824

35 Grew, N. 'On the Attire'. *Anatomy of Plants.* 1682

36 Haighton, Dr. 'Inquiry concerning Animal Impregnation'. *Philosophical Transactions* of the Royal Society. No. 87. 1797

37 Hall, T. *Source Book of Animal Biology.* McGraw-Hill. New York, 1951. Containing the following: 'History of Insects', J. Swammerdam, Trans. T. Hill, Revised J. Hill, p. 368 ff.; 'Theoria Generationis', C. F. Wolff, Trans. M. Hamburger, p. 571 ff.; 'On the Development of Animals', K. E. von Baer, Trans. T. Huxley, p. 392 ff.; 'Contemplation of Nature', C. Bonnet, Trans. J. Wedeny (as 'A Survey of the Wisdom of God in the Creation'), p. 377 ff.; 'General Anatomy Applied to Physiology and Medicine', M. F. X. Bichat, Trans. G. Hayward, pp. 69 and 71.

38 Harvey, William. *The Works of William Harvey* (in one vol.). Trans. R. Willis. Sydenham Society, London, 1847.
(a) 'The Second Disquisition to John Redland'. p. 100 ff.;
(b) 'On Animal Generation'. p. 169 ff.;
(c) 'On the Uterine Membranes and Humours'. p. 551 ff.;
(d) 'On Conception'. p. ff. 573

39 Herbert, W. 'On the Production of Hybrid Vegetables'. *Transactions of the Horticultural Society*. London, 1819

40 Hervé, G. 'Maupertuis Genetiste'. *Revue Anthropologie*. No. 22. 1912

40A Highmore *History of Generation*. London, 1651

41 Kerckring, T. 'An Account of What has of late Been Observed by Dr Kerckringius Concerning the Eggs in Females'. *Philosophical Transactions* of the Royal Society, No. 31. 1672

42 Knight, A. 'Experiments on the Fecundation of Vegetables'. *Philosophical Transactions* of the Royal Society. 1799

43 Koelreuter, J. 'Vorlaeufige Nachricht von Einigen das Geschlecht der Pflanzen betreffenden Beobachtungen'. *Ostwald's Klassiker der Exacten Wissenschaften*. No. 41. Engelmann. Leipzig, 1893

44 Kuhn, T. S. *The Structure of Scientific Revolutions*. University of Chicago Press, 1962

45 Lemery, N. and Winslow, J. B. *Mémoires Académie Royale des Sciences*, Nos. 33, 38 and 40 in 1733, 1738 and 1740

46 Linnaeus, C. 'Disquisitio de Sexu Plantarum'. *Amoenitates Academicae*. Erlangen, 1790. (This was first published in 1760)

47 Lister, M. 'An Objection to the New Hypothesis of the Generation of Animals from Animalcula in Semine Masculino'. *Philosophical Transactions* of the Royal Society, Vol. XX. 1698

48 Lovejoy, A. O. *Essays in the History of Ideas* (note 'On the Discrimination of Romanticisms'). Putnam. New York, 1960

49 —— *The Great Chain of Being*. Reprinted, Harper. New York, 1960

50 Maître-Jan, A. *Observations sur la Formation du Poulet*. Paris, 1722

51 Malpighi, M. (a) *De Formatione Pulli in Ovo*. London, 1672–3
(b) *De Ovo Incubato*. London, 1675

52 Marchant, J. 'Observations sur la Nature des Plantes'. *Mémoires Académie Royale des Sciences*. 1719

53 Meyer, A. W. 'Von Baer and Nature Philosophy' from *Human Generation*. Stamford University Press, 1956

54 Needham, J. *History of Embryology*. 2nd Ed. C.U.P., 1959

55 Needham, Turberville J. 'Observations upon the Generation, Composition, and Decomposition of Animal and Vegetable Substances'. *Philosophical Transactions* of the Royal Society. Vol. XLV, 1750

56 —— *Nouvelles Observations Microscopiques*. Paris, 1750

57 Newton, I. *Principia*. London, 1687. Ed. Florian Cajori. California, 1946

58 Nordenskiold, E. *The History of Biology*. Tudor Publishing Co., New York, 1928

59 Nuck, A. *Adenographia Curiosa et Uteri Foeminei Anatome Nova.* Leiden, 1691

60 Owen, R. 'Remarks on the Entozoa'. *Transactions of the Zoological Society*, Vol. I. 1835

61 Passmore, J. 'William Harvey and the Philosophy of Science'. *Australasian Journal of Philosophy*, Vol. XXXVI. No. 2. Sydney, 1958

62 Pontecorvo, G. *Trends in Genetic Analysis*. Columbia University Press, New York, 1958

Prévost, J. L. (see J. B. Dumas, No. *27*)

63 Randall, J. H., Jr. *The Making of the Modern Mind*. Riverside Press, Cambridge, Mass., 1954

64 Ray, John *Philosophical Transactions* of the Royal Society, Vol. XVII, 1694

65 Redi, F. *Espereinze Intorno alla Generazione degl' Insetti*. Florence, 1688. Translated by M. Bigelow as *Experiments on the Generation of Insects*. Opencourt Publishing Co., Chicago, 1929

66 Roberts, H. F. *Plant Hybridisation before Mendel.* Princeton University Press, 1929

67 Rolando, A. 'Organogénésie'. *Archives Générales de Medecino*, Vol. II. Paris, 1823

68 Roux, W. 'Beitrage zur Entwicklungsmechanik des Embryo Einleitung'. *Zeitschrift fuer Biologie*. W. Kuhne, C. Voit. Munich and Leipzig, 1885. (See also No. *37*)

69 Rudberg, D. *Amoenitates Academicae*. Vol. I. Ed. Haak. Leiden, 1749

70 Sachs, J. *History of Botany*. Trans. Garnsey and Balfour. O.U.P., 1906

Seton, A. (See Goss, J., No. *34*)

71 Spallanzani, L. *Saggio de Observazione Microscopiche Concernante il Systema della Generazione de Needham et Buffon*. Modena, 1765; and *Upuscoli de Fisica Animale et Vegetabile*. Modena, 1776.
Both translated into French as *Œuvres de M. L'Abbé Spallanzani*. Ed. S. Senebier. Paris, 1776;

72 and into English as *Tracts on the Natural History of Animals and Vegetables* by J. Dalyell. 2nd. Ed. Edinburgh, 1803. Vols. I and II.

73 —— *Prodomo di un' Opera Imprimersi Sopre le Reproduzione Animali.* Modena, 1768. Translated into English as *An Essay upon Animal Reproduction* by T. Maty. London, 1769

74 Stadler, L. I. 'The Gene'. *Science*. Vol. 120. 1954

75 Steno, N. *Elementorum Myologiae Specimen*. Florence 1667

76 (Jenson, Nickolas) 'In Ovo et Pullo Observationes'. *Acta Medica Hafniensia*. 1673

77 Swammerdam, Jan *Historia Insectorum Generalis*. Utrecht, 1669. (See also translation in No. 37)

78 —— *Miraculum Naturae sive Uteri Muliebris Fabricae*. Leiden, 1672

79 —— *Book of Nature*. Trans. T. Flloyd. London, 1737

80 Trembley, A. *Mémoires de L'Académie des Sciences*. 1741

81 —— *Philosophical Transactions* of the Royal Society. Vol. XLIII, No. 474, 1744

82 —— *Mémoires pour Servir a l'Histoire d'un Genre de Polypes d'Eau Douce*. Paris and Leiden, 1744

83 Vallisneri, A. *Opere Fisico Mediche*. Vol. I. Venice, 1733

84 Van Horne, J. *Prodromus*. Leiden, 1668

85 von Baer, K. E. (a) *De Ovi Mammalium et Hominis Genesi*. Leipzig, 1827. Translated by C. D. O'Malley in *Isis*. Vol. XLVIII, No. 148. 1956
(b) 'Commentar zu der Schrift: De Ovi Mammalium et Hominis Genesi'. *Zeitschrift fuer Organische Physik*. 1828 (See also Meyer's translation in *53*)

86 'Ueber die Entwicklungsgesichte der Thiere'. *Zeitschrift fuer Organische Physik*. Vol. LI. 1828. (See also Nos. *37* and *53*)

87 von Haller, A. *Elementa Physiologiae*. 8 Vols. Lausanne, 1765–6. (All references to Vol. VIII. *The Foetus*, with special reference to:
(a) Book 29, Section II, Chap. 28: 'Nulla adeo est Epigenesis' (See also No. *54*) and
(b) Book 29 Section II, Chap. 15: 'C. F. Wolff: Vis Essentialis'

88 —— *First Lines of Physiology*. Trans. Cullen (an abridged form of the *Elementa Physiologiae* which was translated into both English and French) 4th Ed. Edinburgh, 1758

89 —— *Sur la Formation du Cœur dans le Poulet*. Lausanne, 1758

90 —— *Réflexions sur le Système de la Génération de M. de Buffon*. Paris and Geneva, 1751

91 —— *Disputationes Selectae: Generatio*. Lausanne, 1750

92 von Leeuwenhoek, A. *Philosophical Transactions:* (a) Vol. XII, 1679; (b) Vol. XIII, 1683; (c) Vol. XV, 1685; (d) Vol. XVI, 1686; (e) Vol. XXI, 1699; (f) Vol. XXII, 1701; (g) Vol. XXV, 1685; (h) Vol. XXXII, 1722

93 —— *Opera Omnia seu Arcana Naturae*. Leiden, 1722. (This reference to Letter 83, 1687)

94 Wharton, T. *Adenographia*. London, 1656

95 Wheeler, W. M. 'C. F. Wolff and the Theoria Generationis'. *Wood's Holl Biological Lectures*. Boston, 1899

96 Whitman, C. O. (a) 'Evolution and Epigenesis'
(b) 'Bonnet's Theory of Evolution'
(c) 'The Pallingenesis and the Germ Doctrine of Bonnet'. *Wood's Holl Biological Lectures*. Boston, 1894–6

97 Willier, Weiss and Hamburger *Analysis of Development*. Saunders, London, 1955

Winslow (See Lemery, No. *45*)

98 Wohl, R. 'Buffon and his Project for a New Science'. *Isis*, Vol. 51, No. 164. 1960

99 Wolff, C. F. 'Theoria Generationis' *Ostwalds Klassiker der Exakten Wissenschaften*, nos. 84 and 85. Leipzig, 1893 and 1896. First appeared in Latin in 1759. (See also No. *37*)

100 —— 'Ueber die Bildung des Darmkanals in Befruchteten Huenchen'. Trans. J. F. Mekel. (Trans. by W. M. Wheeler in 'C. F. Wolff and Theoria Generationis'. See No. *95*)

101 —— 'De Formatione Intestinorum Praeciupue'. *Novi Com Acad Sci Imp Petropol.* 1768

Index